COLLINS PLAYS P

Street Child

by

Berlie Doherty

Resource Material and
Series Consultant

Stephen Cockett

Collins Educational

Published by Collins Educational, an imprint of HarperCollins*Publishers* Ltd,
77–85 Fulham Palace Road, London W6 8JB

© Copyright 2000 playscript Berlie Doherty, resource material Stephen Cockett

First published 2000
Reprinted 2000, 2001 (thrice)

ISBN 000 330 222 9

Berlie Doherty asserts the moral right to be identified as the author of the playscript; Stephen Cockett asserts the moral right to be identified as the author of the resource material.

British Library Cataloguing in Publication Data
A catalogue record for this book is available from the British Library.

Commissioned by Helen Clark, edited by Helen Clark and Toby Satterthwaite, picture research by Charles Evans

Cover design by Chi Leung, cover photograph courtesy Hulton Getty, internal design by Nigel Jordan

Acknowledgements
The following permissions to reproduce material are gratefully acknowledged:
Illustrations: Nigel Jordan, p 73, Hulton Getty Picture Library, p78, 84; The Salvation Army, p80; Barnardo's Picture Library, p89, 91, 92, 96–7; PA Photos, pp 104, 109.
Text extracts: Something Accepted Something Done by T.J. Barnardo was first published by Shaw and Co, p79; *Mayhew's Characters* (ed. Peter Quennell) was first published by Spring Books, Hamlyn Publishing Group (1967), pp81–2, 84; *Ordinary Lives* by Carol Adams, Virago, 1982, p82; *Parental Care for the Salvation of Children* was first published by The Religious Tract Society, 1839, p86; *The Parlour Song Book* edited by Michael Turner, Penguin, 1972, p88; *Father of Nobody's Children* by Norman Wymer, Arrow Books, 1954, p90, 94; 'Children of the Tunnels' by Louise Branson, Maclean's Magazine, 1993, pp107–8; 'Mission Possible' Newsletter, Mission Possible, 1999, p109; Barnardo's Leaflet, Barnardo's, p 111.

Whilst every effort has been made both to contact the copyright holders, this has not proved possible in every case.

printed and bound by Imago in Singapore

For permission to perform this play, please allow plenty of time and contact:
Permissions Department, HarperCollins*Publishers*,
77–85 Fulham Palace Road, London W6 8JB. Tel. 0181 741 7070.

Contents

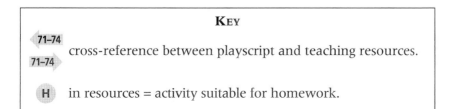

KEY
71–74 cross-reference between playscript and teaching resources. **71–74**
H in resources = activity suitable for homework.

Characters

THE JARVIS HOUSEHOLD

JIM JARVIS the youngest child of a poor family
EMILY Jim's sister
LIZZIE Jim's sister
MA their mother
MR SPINK the landlord

THE BIG HOUSE

ROSIE Ma's friend
JUDD the housekeeper
COOK a servant
POLLY a maid

THE WORKHOUSE

JOSEPH an inmate
MR SISSONS master of the workhouse
MRS SISSONS mistress of the workhouse
MR BARRACK a teacher
MARION an inmate
FLO an inmate
ELSIE an inmate
BESSIE an inmate
JOHNNY a boy in the workhouse
TIP a boy in the workhouse

THE STREET

SHRIMPS a street child and friend of Jim's
MUVVER Shrimps's mother
BILLY a street child

DAVEY a street child
SAMUEL a watchman
MAUDIE a coffee-seller
GRANDMOTHER Rosie's grandmother
GRANDFATHER Rosie's grandfather
LAME BETSY Rosie's friend

GRIMY NICK'S

GRIMY NICK a coal lighterman
MR COCKERILL a coal merchant
JOSH a sailor
BARMAID at the Waterman's Arms
SILAS an old man drinking at the Waterman's
MINNIE a field child
ALFIE a field child
KITTY a field child

THE CIRCUS

JUGLINI the circus owner
MADAME JUGLINI Juglini's wife
MARIA their daughter
ANTONIO their son

OTHER CHARACTERS

DR BARNARDO a missionary
and teacher at a ragged shool
MRS HODDER a shopkeeper
WOMAN in the street
SECOND WOMAN in the street
POLICEMAN
CART BOY
BIG BOYS at the workhouse
POSH LADY
MAN in the crowd
WOMAN in the crowd
BEGGAR
WOMAN HAWKER a street trader
GENTLEMAN
CHILDREN (3) at the ragged school

ALSO:
STREET CHILDREN
SHOPPERS
HAWKERS
WORKHOUSE CHILDREN
WORKHOUSE PATIENTS
CIRCUS PERFORMERS

Setting

London in the 1860s. The play has several locations and would generally work without sets or props, although set areas could be established – for instance, Dr Barnardo's study. Setting directions to create atmosphere are given throughout the play.

There is a large cast suitable for school play purposes, though several are very small speaking parts and could be spoken by one character within a group of, say, street children, field children etc. Many of the characters appear in only one of the three acts and could therefore be doubled. Jim has a very big part which could be played by two boys, one in Doctor Barnardo's study.

Street Child

ACT ONE
Scene One

London in the 1860s. The sound of carters and horse-drawn carriages. Cries 74 *of 'Laces for sale' 'Hot steaming coffee!' and 'Whelkso, shrimpso!' Ragged children run across the stage, stealing from the vendors' carts and barrows. At the side of the stage is a room (Barnardo's study), lit by an oil lamp and firelight. Lights come up on a man (**Dr Barnardo**) writing at a desk and a boy (**Jim Jarvis**) sitting by the fire, warming his hands. Street sounds fade as Jim stands up and addresses the audience.*

JIM *(to audience)* Jim Jarvis. Want to know who that is? It's me! That's my name. Only thing I've got, is my name. And I've give it away to this man. Barnie, his name is, or something like that. He told me once, only I forgot it, see, and I don't like to ask him again. 'Mister', I call him, to his face that is. But there's a little space in my head where his name is Barnie.

BARNARDO *(with a slight Irish accent)* Now, Jim. Are you going to tell me your story?

JIM My story, Mister? What d'you want to know that for? Ain't much of a story, mine ain't.

BARNARDO Oh, it is, Jim. It is. It's a very special story. It changed my life, child, meeting you.

JIM *(to audience)* Funny that, ain't it? Because he changed my life, Barnie did. I can't believe my luck, and that's a fact. Here I am with food in my belly, and good hot food at that, and plenty more where that came from, he says. There's just me and him, special. I want to laugh. I'm so full of something that I want to laugh out loud!

BARNARDO Just tell me your story.

JIM I don't know where to begin, and that's a fact.

BARNARDO Start with your mother.

JIM My ma? I can hardly remember my ma. But when I think about her, I can hear her talking to me, all soft and gentle. And then one day, everything changed.

BARNARDO And when was that?

JIM It was the day she sent me out to buy a meat pudding.

Scene Two

*Mrs Hodder's Pudding and Pie Shop. **Mrs Hodder** is brushing sawdust across the floor of her shop. Ragged **boys** peer through the window. She shoos them away cheerfully. **Jim** runs in, panting.*

MRS HODDER You can run right out again! If I'm not sick of little boys today!

JIM But I've come to buy a pudding! I've got a shilling, look!

MRS HODDER (*bites the coin*) Where did you find this, little shrimp? And stop your dancing! You're making me rock like a ship at sea!

JIM Ma's purse. And she said there won't be no more, because that's the last shilling we got, and I know that's true because I emptied her purse for her. So make it a good one, Mrs Hodder. Make it big, and lots of gravy!

MRS HODDER Here you are now. Careful, it's hot. I'll wrap it in a cloth for you. Now run home quick, before those thieving varmints pinch it off you!

She watches him, shaking her head sadly as he runs off with the pie pressed against his chest.

Scene Three

*A dingy room in a tenement block. **Ma** is lying on a pile of rags, asleep.*
*Jim's sisters, **Lizzie** and **Emily**, are sitting each side of her, holding her*
*hands. **Jim** bursts in, panting with triumph and excitement.*

Jim I've got the pie! I've got the pie!

Emily Sssh! Ma's asleep, Jim. Bring it over here.

They break off chunks of pastry and eat hungrily with their fingers.

Lizzie What about Ma?

Emily She won't want it. She never eats.

Lizzie But the gravy might do her good. Just a little taste. Stop
shovelling it down so fast, Jim. Let Ma have a bit. Here Ma, try a
bit. It's lovely!

Ma shakes her head and turns over, coughing, huddling her rug round her.

Jim I'll have it!

Lizzie Leave it, Jim. She might feel like it later. The smell might
tempt her.

Emily I told you, she don't want food no more. That's what she
said.

Jim What's the matter with her, Emily?

Emily Nothing's the matter.

Lizzie She's tired, is all. She just wants to sleep, don't she?

Jim But she's been asleep all day. And yesterday. And the day
before.

Emily Just eat your pie. You heard what she said. There's no more
shillings in that purse, so don't expect no more pies after this
one.

LIZZIE She'll get better soon. And then she'll be able to get more money. We'll soon be out of this place. That's what she told me, Jim.

JIM Will we go back to our cottage?

LIZZIE You know we can't go there. We had to move out when Father died.

EMILY Eat your pie. She wants us to enjoy it. And then go to sleep.

*The **children** eat slowly, thoughtfully. They pull their rags round themselves and huddle up, **Lizzie** with **Jim** and **Emily** with **Ma**.*

LIZZIE Emily, what's going to happen to us?

EMILY Ssh Lizzie. No point worrying. We'll be all right when Ma gets better.

LIZZIE But what if she don't get better? Not for ages?

EMILY We'll manage. We'll have to. Now go to sleep.

JIM I can hear something tapping!

***Emily** sits up, aware of the sound of a tapping stick. Now all the children sit up, listening.*

EMILY *(whispers)* The Stick Man!

75 *A cane raps against the door. The door is flung open and in strides **Mr Spink**, the landlord, stamping snow off his boots.*

MR SPINK I did knock. But when lie-abeds don't answer then lie-abeds must be got up.

*The **children** scramble to their feet, standing in a line to protect **Ma**. **Mr Spink** peers over their heads at her.*

MR SPINK Is she dead?

EMILY No sir, she ain't dead.

MR SPINK Sick then?

EMILY No sir, she ain't sick neither.

Jim looks at her in surprise.

MR SPINK Then if she ain't dead nor sick, what's she doing down there? Lying under the covers like a grand lady with nothing to do! Hiding is she? Counting all her money?

Mr Spink pushes the children out of the way and lifts up the rag pile with his cane.

EMILY Leave her, sir. She's tired out, she's been working that hard. She'll be off out to work again soon.

JIM But Emily…!

Lizzie clutches his hand warningly.

MR SPINK If she's been working, she can pay her rent, and we'll all be happy. Up you get, woman!

*Ma struggles to sit up, helped by **Lizzie**.*

MR SPINK Where's your money, Mrs Jarvis? (*He sees the purse bag on the floor. He leans down towards **Jim**, who backs away from his wheezy breath.*) I'm an old man, and I don't bend. Pick up that purse for me, sonny.

*Jim holds the purse at arm's length for **Mr Spink** to take.*

MR SPINK Is it empty, sonny? Empty? What's that nice smell? (*pretending surprise*) Did you eat pie last night? Did you, sonny?

JIM Yes.

MR SPINK Was it a lovely meat pie, all hot and full of gravy?

JIM I don't know.

Mr Spink picks up the pudding cloth with his stick.

JIM I bought it. It was Ma's last shilling, but I bought the pie.

EMILY *(softly)* Oh Jim!

MR SPINK Ma's last shilling, was it? No money. Oh dear. No money, no rent. No rent, no room, Mrs Jarvis. Oh dear.

MA *(weakly)* We've nowhere else to go.

JIM Ma, couldn't we go back to the cottage? I liked it better there.

MR SPINK Your cottage! When you came crawling to me twelve months ago you was glad of this place, make no mistake about it. But if you like a cottage better, find yourself a father, and let him pay for one. Can you do that?

MA Give us a little longer, and we'll pay our rent. The girls can help me.

MR SPINK I've made up my mind, Mrs Jarvis. I'm a charitable man, as you know. I've a family wants to move in here tonight. There's eight of them – don't they deserve a home now? And what's more – they can pay me for it! Out!

He goes, his stick tap-tapping into silence. **Ma** *struggles up and puts her arms round* **Lizzie** *and* **Jim**. **Emily** *bundles their rags together, picks up a toy wooden horse and gives it to* **Jim**.

EMILY Here, keep it safe. It's the last thing Father made you. And you might as well have Lizzie's boots. They're too small for her now.

The **children** *stand in the doorway clutching their bundles while* **Ma** *ties her bonnet and fastens her shawl round herself. She moves slowly and quietly.*

EMILY Where can we go?

MA I'll find us a home. Don't worry.

LIZZIE Not the workhouse!

MA No, not the workhouse. I'd rather die in the street than go there. I'm going to take you to see the only friend I've got in the world. Rosie, she's called. You've heard me talk about Rosie, when I used to work at his Lordship's?

LIZZIE Are we going to live in the Big House?

EMILY It'd be too grand for the likes of us, Lizzie.

MA I'll have to trust you to be good.

LIZZIE What do you mean, Ma? Of course we'll be good.

MA I know you will. At least I got that right. God help you girls. Come on now. If Rosie can't help us, nobody can.

They go.

Scene Four

The kitchen of the Big House. A large table with a couple of chairs. **Rosie,**
the maid, is making bread, puffing and grumbling, thumping the dough.

ROSIE Run off me feet I am. I'm no cook. Should be upstairs doing me proper job, dusting the rooms. They'll be sorry they ever asked me to bake bread. Break their teeth on it, they will.

There is a knock at the outside door. **Rosie** *opens it.*

ROSIE Annie Jarvis! I never thought I'd see you again! Come in, all of you, and get yourselves warm. But don't make no noise. You know what they're like upstairs.

Emily *helps* **Ma** *in and sits her in a chair.* **Lizzie** *and* **Jim** *follow, shy.*

ROSIE You ain't come looking for work have you, after all this time? Cook's going spare, she is, looking for someone to help her. She's got me at it, and my dough's like a boulder – you could build cathedrals out of it, and they wouldn't ever fall down! Look at you! You've been turned out, haven't you? You got anywhere to go?

MA No. We'll find somewhere.

13

Rosie And you're not fit for work. I can see that plain as my nose. There's no work left in you, Annie Jarvis.

A bell jangles over the door.

Rosie Lord, that's for the coffees, and I ain't done them. If anyone comes down, you children duck under the table quick, mind. *(bell rings again)* All right, all right, his lordship can wait five minutes, can't he, while I talk to my friend here? My sister, as good as. There's only one home left to you now, Annie. It's the House, ain't it, heaven help you. The workhouse! *(bell rings again)* No, he can't wait. His lordship waits for nothing.

Ma Help Rosie out with her bread, Emily. It'd be a good turn that she'd appreciate.

Rosie Aye, and his lordship would too!

*Rosie runs out of the house door with a tray of coffee. **Emily** washes her hands and kneads the dough.*

Ma Nice and firm now, like I've taught you. Plenty of flour. And don't let any air bubbles in.

Emily I know, Ma.

*Judd, the housekeeper, enters through the house door. **Jim** hides under the table. **Judd** watches **Emily**. **Rosie** rejoins them, winking at **Ma**.*

Judd Rosie tells me you're in a bad way, Annie Jarvis. And I must say, you look it.

Ma I haven't come to make trouble, Judd. And I'm sorry if I've interrupted the work. I've only come to say goodbye to you and Rosie, because you've always been so kind to me.

Judd If we've been kind to you it's because you've always done your work well, and that's what matters. You can cook, can you, girl?

Ma She can cook as well as I can. And she can scrub the floor for you and run errands. She can sleep on the kitchen floor and take up no room.

Rosie She wouldn't need paying. She'd be a saving, Judd.

Judd I couldn't do anything for the other girl.

Rosie Judd, I've a sister who's cook at Sunbury. She might give her a chance. If you just let little Lizzie sleep down here with Emily till Sunday, and I can walk her over to Moll's then.

Judd I don't want to know they're here, Rosie. If his lordship finds out, it's every one of us for the workhouse. You know that, don't you? I don't know they're here, these girls. *(she goes)*

Rosie It's the best I can do to help you, Annie. I can't do no more.

Ma It's more than I expected. At least you've saved my girls from that place. *(she looks round for Jim and he crawls out from under the table)* We'd better go. It's not fair to Rosie if we stay here any longer.

Lizzie Ma, don't leave us here!

Emily puts her arm round Lizzie's shoulder. Ma hugs them both.

Ma I have to, I have to. This is best for you. God bless you, both of you. Jim, say goodbye to your sisters. I don't suppose you'll ever see them again.

Jim Can't I stay with them?

Emily and Lizzie hug Jim. Rosie looks away, blowing her nose on her apron. Ma takes Jim's hand and bundles him quickly out of the door.

Scene Five

A London street. Women hawkers crying their wares. Children playing with hoops. A boy is brushing the street. A gentleman gives him a coin and the boy brushes a way clear for him. Jim helps Ma along, trudging and stopping.

Jim There's a fountain over there. Shall I get you some water?

Ma I can't go any further. God help you, Jim. *(she collapses)*

JIM Ma! Ma, wake up! You can't go to sleep here. Ma, please wake up. *(he puts her rug over her)* Will you help me? Will you help me? My Ma's sick.

*People walk past, ignoring them. A **child** sneaks up and takes **Jim's** toy horse.*

WOMAN Give him his horse back. It's all he's got, ain't it? A pair of boots what's too big for him, and a wooden horse. Give it back.

*The **children** laugh and run off with the toy.*

SECOND WOMAN Get them to the workhouse. There's nothing we can do for her.

WOMAN I'm not taking them there. Prison would be better than there. Tell this bobby we caught the boy stealing, and let him put them both in prison.

***Policeman** approaches and people scatter.*

POLICEMAN What's going on?

JIM I ain't stolen nothing.

POLICEMAN Get up, boy. And you, woman. Get up!

JIM She can't. She's sick.

*The **policeman** clicks his fingers and a **boy** runs up with a cart.*

POLICEMAN Put her in the cart. She can't stop here.

*The **policeman** and the **boy** lift **Ma** into the cart. **Jim** watches, afraid.*

CART BOY Where to?

POLICEMAN Take 'em to the workhouse. Let 'em die in there.

*The **cart boy** trundles the cart off, whistling, and **Jim** stumbles after him.*

Scene Six

*The Workhouse. A huge, gloomy building lit dimly by candles. The **inmates** shuffle silently, all dressed in identical clothes. A bell rings. **Joseph** shuffles along carrying a lantern. He opens the door to the **cart boy**, **Ma** and **Jim**.*

CART BOY Two more for you. One for the infirmary, one for school.

JOSEPH Not another cholera case, is she? Mister Sissons won't want her here if she is.

CART BOY She won't last long. I'll come back tomorrow for my cart.

*He goes. **Joseph** wheels the cart inside, sighing.*

JOSEPH Come on boy. No use hanging about there. Come on in.

*Jim follows him. The door closes behind him. **Mr Sissons** enters, creating a shiver of apprehension. **Mrs Sissons** and **Marion** bring on a trestle table and cauldrons of food.*

JOSEPH Two more guests, Mister Sissons.

MR SISSONS Take the woman straight upstairs, Joseph. We don't want her spreading her nasty germs in here.

JOSEPH Right-oh, Mister Sissons.

*He wheels **Ma** off.*

JIM Where's Ma going?

MRS SISSONS Where's she going? Infirmary, that's where she's going. Wants feeding and medicine, no doubt, and nothing to buy it with neither.

JIM Can I go with her?

MRS SISSONS Go with her? A big strong boy like you? You cannot! If you're good, Mr Sissons might let you see her tomorrow. Good, mind! Know what good means? Now go with Marion and get yourself scrubbed and cropped.

17

Mr Sissons And show him the boy-cage first. Just in case he gets any ideas into his head.

Marion You come with me. The boy-cage is where they puts the boys what try to run away from here. They catch 'em and beat 'em and stick 'em in there till they're good. Remember that.

*She leads **Jim** off. **Boys** dressed identically and **girls** in coarse dresses file in holding bowls. **Mrs Sissons** ladles out gruel to some of them. She stops by a coughing **boy**.*

Mrs Sissons No, you're not having any, with a cough like that. Cod liver oil for you, my boy. And none for you. I don't like the look on your face today.

*Another boy, **Johnny**, grabs a piece of bread. **Mr Sissons** drags him out of the queue.*

Mr Sissons Misbehavin', were you? Acting like a pig? Well, you can eat like a pig. Food in the trough for this boy, Mrs Sissons.

***Mrs Sissons** ladles out gruel and puts the bowl on the floor. **Mr Sissons** makes **Johnny** kneel with his hands behind his back and forces his face into it.*

Mr Sissons Let us reflect for a moment, children, on the poor people outside these gates who will have no food at all tonight. Let us always thank God for the charity that is shown within these walls.

Children *(dully)* Yes, Mister Sissons.

***Jim** comes back in dressed in workhouse clothes. **Tip**, a boy with wild hair, grins at **Jim**. **Marion** returns to help **Mrs Sissons**.*

Tip *(whispers)* I'm Tip, I am. What's your name?

***Mr Sissons** lifts **Tip** up by the collar.*

Mr Sissons Did you speak, boy? Did I tell you to speak? No food for this mouth, Mrs Sissons. It's too full of words. Children, put your hands together in prayer and show this new boy how we thank the Lord for our good fortune.

CHILDREN *(raggedly)* We give thanks to the Lord for our food and our home and the kindness we are shown. Amen.

TIP Amen.

Mr Sissons strikes him. The trestle, bowls and cauldron are removed by Mrs Sissons and Marion. Mr Sissons goes. Marion returns with a candle.

MARION Bed. Quickly.

The children curl up to go to sleep.

JIM Can I go to my ma?

MARION No you cannot. You've got to go to sleep like the other boys.

JIM I can't sleep.

MARION What's up with you?

JIM I want Ma. I want Emily and Lizzie.

MARION You're warm and dry, ain'tcha? Thank God for that, and go to sleep.

She blows out her candle and sits down. Music or song here from Marion or Jim, OR dream sequence in which Ma, Emily and Lizzie hold hands and dance around Jim, and then go. Morning light.

MARION Look, it's morning already. I can hear Joseph out in the yard. You've kept me awake all night, you have.

She goes, yawning.

JOSEPH *(hobbles in)* Five of the clock and time to get up. Run off out to the yard and scrub your mucky faces. I've already broken the ice round the pump, so no thinking you can dodge it.

*Groaning, the **boys** yawn and stretch and run outside.*

JIM Please sir...

JOSEPH Get yerself washed quick, boy. Afore the wevver bites me bones off.

JIM Sir...

JOSEPH I'm not sir. I'm only doing my turn, like the rest of them. I'm only Joseph, not sir. I hate sir, same as you.

JIM Please Joseph, tell me where the infirmary is.

JOSEPH Why should I tell you that?

JIM Because my ma's there, and I've been good. Mrs Sissons said if I was good I could go and see Ma in the infirmary today.

JOSEPH So you was the boy as came in last night, and your ma was brought on a cart?

JIM Yes. So please tell me where the infirmary is.

JOSEPH Well, it's upstairs. *(he hesitates)* Only the message I was given by Mrs Sissons is, don't bother taking the boy up there, because his ma... Your ma's dead, son.

He walks away.

JIM Ma? Ma's dead? Don't cry, Jim. Don't cry in here. Not in here. I want Rosie. I want to tell Emily and Lizzie. I won't cry. Not in here.

***Joseph** comes back in with **Tip** and **Johnny**.*

JOSEPH Now don't go upsetting that boy. He's had bad news.

JIM I want to go home.

JOSEPH Home? What d'you mean, home? What's this, if it ain't home? It's the whole world, this place is. Whole world.

***Tip** and **Johnny** laugh.*

TIP It ain't, Joseph. There's no shops here, and no carriages. And no trees.

JOHNNY And there's no river. There's a great big river outside here.

JOSEPH Is there now? I should like to see that river. Though to tell the truth, boys, I don't know what a river is. I was born here, I was. Only home I knows. Tell you something. I don't want to die in here. If someone will let me know what day I'm going to die, I'll be grateful. I'll climb over that wall first. Yes. That's what I'll do. *(Joseph notices that **Tip** and **Johnny** are laughing at him)* Go on, off to the schoolroom and get some learning done. Off you go.

*Tip and **Johnny** run off and **Joseph** follows, sweeping them with a brush.*

JIM My home, is it? My home, this place? Well, it ain't. I'll get out of here quick as I can, and I'll run and run till I find Lizzie and Emily, and we'll find us a proper home. Live here? No Jim, you won't. And you're not going to cry here, not for Ma, not for anyone. Not here Jim. Not here. This ain't your home, this ain't. And never will be.

He goes. Music or song here.

Scene Seven

The schoolroom. A long, dim room with candles set into every other desk.
*The little window is painted over. There is a fireplace at one end with sheets steaming round it. Four women, **Marion**, **Elsie**, **Bessie** and **Flo** hang washing up round the fire. There are four big arches across the ceiling with words on them: 'God is good, God is holy, God is just, God is love'. The **boys** file to their desks and sit shivering while the old schoolmaster, **Mr Barrack**, paces up and down the aisles, thumping the desks with a knotted rope.*

BARRACK I don't like noise in my classroom. What don't I like?

BOYS Noise, Mister Barrack.

BARRACK Speak up. What don't I like?

BOYS *(shouting)* NOISE, MISTER BARRACK.

21

BARRACK What?

WOMEN BOYS, MISTER BARRACK.

BARRACK That's better.

Jim comes in.

BARRACK Late! Come and be punished.

JIM I didn't know the way, mister.

BARRACK Speak up.

BOYS He didn't know the way, mister.

BARRACK Speak up.

WOMEN *(roar)* HE DIDN'T KNOW THE WAY, MISTER.

BARRACK Are you new?

JIM Yes, mister.

BARRACK Are you good? Or are you evil?

JIM I don't know, mister.

BARRACK What is he, boys?

BOYS Evil, Mister Barrack.

BARRACK And what would he like to be?

BOYS Good, Mister Barrack.

BESSIE Bless him, he don't know what evil means, that child don't.

*Mr Barrack points to a place next to **Tip**. **Jim** sits down.*

BARRACK Read me the ceiling!

*Tip stands up and bows to the **women**, holding out his hands.*

FLO & BESSIE God is good, God is holy.

ELSIE & MARION God is just, God is love.

BESSIE Six cobwebs and nine dead flies.

*The **women** all roar with laughter. **Tip** joins in.*

BARRACK There's nothing to laugh at here.

TIP No sir, there ain't.

BARRACK Tell this miserable little new boy what the most important part of our day is.

*The **women** mime eating, getting more and more extravagant as they pretend to have plates piled high with food.*

TIP *(laughing)* Eating, sir.

BARRACK No it ain't.

TIP You're right sir, it ain't. Food's so bad it ain't worth eating anyway.

*The **women** shriek with laughter.*

MARION I agree, and I'm the one that cooks it!

FLO Don't you hit him, Mister Barrack. He's a good boy.

BESSIE That's right, he is. He agrees with everything you say!

BARRACK Boys, tell this ignorant child what the most important part of the day is.

BOYS *(dully)* Prayer, sir.

BARRACK If that is all you ever learn, you will have done well. Get your slates out, and write.

*The **boys** start writing immediately.*

TIP Please, Mister Barrack. What should we write?

BARRACK Speak up!

TIP What should we write?

BARRACK What should you write? The Lord's Prayer, if you please!

*The **boys** scribble industriously, except for **Jim**, who is sitting with his head in his hands.*

TIP Why ain'tcha writing?

JIM 'Cos I can't. I never knew how to write.

TIP Cor, it's easy! Just wiggle your chalk across the slate like this. There! Now blow your dust off, and you've got writing. See!

JIM That's good. What does it say though?

TIP I don't know! I can't read!

Jim laughs.

BARRACK Did you laugh then?

TIP No he didn't. It was me.

*Barrack swings the rope across **Tip's** hand.*

BARRACK *(to Jim)* Stand up! What did he say to you?

JIM He said he can't read, mister.

WOMEN *(shout)* HE CAN'T READ, MISTER.

BARRACK Can't read! Can't read! I'll say he can't read. What's the use of teaching boys like him to read? What do any of you want with reading or writing, miserable sinners that you are? Do as you're told, and write!

Jim scribbles furiously.

TIP *(whispers)* Don't worry about me. I'd have got hit anyway. Once Barrack starts hitting you, Barrack always hits you. Every day if he can.

JIM *(whispers)* Did it hurt?

TIP Nah. Just don't let him have a chance to start. Tell Barrack Tip did it, if he blames you for anything. Tip'll get hit anyway, so you might as well.

*Some of the **boys** stand up and begin to sing a hymn, very sweetly, based on the words 'God is good, God is holy, God is just, God is love'. **Barrack** smiles and conducts them. Other **boys** take instruments out of their desks and begin to accompany them.*

ELSIE Ain't that sweet! Brings tears to me eyes, that does.

*The **women** join in the hymn. **Tip** begins beating a drum and chanting a savage counter melody, which gradually the **boys** take up.*

TIP I hate school. I hate school. I hate this place. I hate this place.

*The **women** cover up their ears and run out.*

JIM *(shouts or sings over the noise)* I want Ma! I want Lizzie! I want Emily! I want to go home. I want to go home!

Scene Eight

*A bare yard surrounded by high walls. **Jim** and **Tip** and a few other boys are sweeping. They are shivering.*

JIM How long have I been here, Tip?

TIP How should I know? Keep moving, Jim. It's cold.

JIM We had a long time of being very cold, and shivering all night. And then we was too hot, and these clothes was all itchy and heavy. And now it's cold again, and there's ice on the pump. I've been here a year. Tip, I'm going to run away. Come with me?

TIP Don't be mad. You've seen what happens to the boys who try. They get put in the boy-cage. They thrash 'em every day until they're good.

JIM Only if they catches 'em.

TIP They always catch 'em. Bobbies catch 'em and bring 'em in, and they get thrashed and thrashed.

JIM If I don't try to get away, I'll be like Joseph. One day I won't remember whether I was born here or not. I won't know anywhere but here. Won't you come with me?

TIP I daresn't. Honest, I daresn't. Don't go, Jim.

JIM I've got to. And I'm going tonight, Tip.

*Joseph shuffles in, followed by other **children**.*

JOSEPH Keep busy, keep busy. Sir's coming.

*Mr Sissons enters, accompanied by **Mrs Sissons**, who cuffs the **children** as she passes them.*

MR SISSONS Who's not working? Who's slacking today?

MRS SISSONS They're all slacking, Mister Sissons.

MR SISSONS Then they've got time for some real work, Mrs Sissons. I'm looking for some big boys. To help the carpet-beaters.

MRS SISSONS Just as I would expect. A rush to help.

MR SISSONS And the place is full of sickness, Mrs Sissons. What do they care? It might be cholera, my dears. Cholera, striking us all down like ninepins. Do they care? I've got two thousand mouths to feed here, and someone has to earn the money, cholera or not. Somebody has to buy the medicines. Somebody has to pay for the burials.

MRS SISSONS Plenty of big strong boys here, eating every crumb I give them, and never a word of thanks.

*Mr and Mrs Sissons walk along the rows, cuffing the biggest **boys** on the backs of their heads as they pass them, and pulling them to the front.*

Mr Sissons I want all the big boys upstairs in the infirmary straight away, and you don't come down again till all the carpets are done. Understand?

Big Boys Yes, Mister Sissons.

*Mr and Mrs Sissons leave, leading the **big boys**.*

Jim What's carpets?

Tip Dunno. They get sent here from the rich houses, that I do know. The women here beat 'em, and then they send them back. That's what I've heard.

Jim They get sent back to the big houses?

Tip Far as I know. A man comes with a cart to collect them.

Jim I'm going to help.

Tip A daft boy, you are. He asked for big boys.

Jim You coming or not? *(**Jim** darts off after the **big boys**)*

Tip Oh, all right. Wait for me, though. *(**Tip** runs after him)*

Scene Nine

*The Ward. **Patients** are lying in beds. A line is strung across the room with carpets hanging from it. **Bessie**, **Marion**, **Flo** and **Elsie** and **big boys** hit the carpets with flattened sticks. In their beds the **patients** gasp and cough and beg for water. **Jim** and **Tip** enter.*

Jim I think this must be where Ma died.

Tip Is it? Don't know where my Ma is, I don't.

They pick up the beaters and make feeble attempts to beat the carpets.

Bessie Now who sent you two along! Might as well get a pair of spiders to come and do the job!

FLO Big strong boys, that's what we want for this work, ain't it, Marion?

Jim staggers and lets the beating-stick drop.

JIM We're really strong, though. Look at my muscles! And we'd do anything to help Mister Sissons, wouldn't we, Tip?

MARION You're supposed to thrash the carpets, not tickle them.

BESSIE Needs a Ma, he does. Like I need a little boy. Lost mine. Soon as I came in here, lost my little boy.

ELSIE But who'd want to bring up a child in here, eh?

TIP Come on, Jim. We'd better go back to the oakum room and do our sacks.

JIM But we want to help. We could carry the carpets to the door. We're good at carrying, ain't we, Tip?

BESSIE Are you? Now you're talking! Floppy things, is carpets. I could do with a bit of help with this one here. You two take the other end. Here we go, out that far door.

*Bessie lifts up a rolled-up carpet and **Jim** and **Tip** lift the other end. Between them they carry a carpet to the door. **Mrs Sissons** is sitting by the doorway knitting a black shawl.*

TIP Jim. Mrs Sissons is there.

JIM Take no notice. Just act normal.

TIP Me heart's banging like a big drum. Can't you hear it?

JIM Ssh! Just keep going.

*Without looking at them, **Mrs Sissons** unlocks the door.*

BESSIE That's it boys. We'll just leave the carpet outside here for the man to pick up.

*They lower the carpet down and **Bessie** turns away.*

JIM Tip. Can you see? The outside gate's open. I can hear the carriages on the street, and the horses, and the people. It's easy, Tip. We can do it easy.

TIP I daresn't. I daresn't.

JIM I'm going. I'm going now, Tip. Now's me chance, and I've got to take it.

TIP Don't forget me, Jim.

Jim runs. Sound of gates clanging behind him.

*The stage goes black, with just **Jim** lit up, running.*

JIM I did it! I did it! I'm free!

ACT TWO
Scene One

The street. It is dusk, and people are bustling past on their way home. A boy, **Shrimps**, *is selling bootlaces. Jim enters, very cold and tired.* **Shrimps** *pretends to doff his cap at* **Jim**.

SHRIMPS Bootlaces, mister! Three for the price of two! You don't want three, Sir? Well, two for the price of three then, can't say fairer than that, can I?

He squats next to **Jim** *and offers him a bit of crust from his pocket.*

SHRIMPS Here. Have a bit of crust. You from the workhouse?

JIM Nah.

SHRIMPS Bet you are. Them's workhouse clothes, ain't they? Been there meself. They look warm, mind you.

JIM I'll swop you. Give us your clothes, and you can have mine.

SHRIMPS And get picked up by the bobbies for running away! Not likely, bruvver. You have run away, haven't you? Don't worry, I won't tell no-one. You got somewhere to go?

JIM Yes. I'm going to find Emily. She's my sister. Only I don't know where she lives.

SHRIMPS Well that's helpful, bruvver, that is.

JIM She's with Rosie someone. In a big house. By a fountain. A road with a fountain at the end of it. And a bootscraper at the door that looks like a dog. And I've been all over London looking for it.

SHRIMPS Well you ain't looked hard enough. Fountain. What's that over there, bruvver? *(he runs off swinging his laces over his head)* Laces! Laces! Laces, mister? Best in town.

JIM That's it! This is the fountain where I tried to give Ma a drink. And there's the Big House with the bootscraper that looks like a dog. I've found it. I've found Emily! Everything will be all right now.

Scene Two

The kitchen of the Big House. **Cook** *is sewing by the table.* **Polly**, *a maid, is sweeping the floor. There is an urgent hammering at the door.*

COOK Gracious me, frightened the living daylights out of me. Answer it Polly, then you can get off to bed.

JIM *(outside)* Emily! Emily!

POLLY Hang on, I'm coming. *(she opens the door and tries to close it again)* We don't give to beggars.

JIM I'm not a beggar. I've come to see Emily.

POLLY Emily? There's no Emily here.

JIM Emily Jarvis. She helps Rosie out in the kitchen.

POLLY Rosie? Who's she?

COOK What does he want, Polly?

JIM Rosie. You must know Rosie. She's got big arms. And she don't like making bread.

POLLY Hear that, cook? There's no-one here who doesn't like making bread, is there?

JIM But it was this house. It was this kitchen, I know it was. Tell me where Emily is, please.

POLLY You'll have to go, sonny. You've snooped round for long enough, I reckon.

JIM I ain't snooping. I'm looking for my sister. There was a lady with a black crinkly dress, called Judd. She'll remember.

COOK Judd! She was the last housekeeper. She was sent away. And there was another woman. She might have been called Rosie, now I come to think of it. I got her job. They were found hiding some street children in the kitchen, and his lordship dismissed them both.

JIM They were my sisters, Emily and Lizzie. Please miss, where are they? Where's Rosie?

Cook stands up and comes to the doorway.

COOK Are they workhouse clothes?

JIM Please don't send me back there.

COOK I wouldn't send my worst enemy there. All right, you can come in for a bit. *(she leads Jim into the kitchen)* You go off to bed, Polly. I'll put him on his way.

Polly seems to think it's all a fine joke.

POLLY Goodnight, sweetheart.

She tweaks Jim's cap over his eye and takes her candle up the side stairs.

COOK Sit by the fire, boy. Where I can keep an eye on you. Lucky for you, his lordship's away for the night. If he was here you wouldn't set foot over this doorstep, or we'd all be off to the workhouse. And lucky for you I've decided to stay up and get this sewing done. And don't think you can pinch anything. And lucky for you there's a bit of stew left, too. Could you eat it?

JIM Thanks, Missus.

He eats rapidly then falls asleep.

COOK Don't you dare move from that spot. You can stay here till morning comes. Soon as the dairywoman comes, you're on her cart and away, and you're never coming back. That right? Look at him, poor soul. Out like a light. Ah well, *(yawns)* he's not going to pinch anything while he's asleep, that's for sure. Might as well take a nap myself.

She blows out the candle and sleeps. Outside, watchman Samuel taps on the window.

SAMUEL Half past five, time to be alive!

Lights come up.

LAME BETSY *(calls from outside)* Milko! Creamo!

COOK Here's Lame Betsy now. Wake up child. You've got to go with her.

Lame Betsy enters from the street door carrying a jug of milk.

BETSY Here you are, just one jug today, was it? Oh, I see you've got visitors. Know where he's come from.

COOK This boy is looking for Rosie, who used to work here. If I'm right, she's a friend of yours, Betsy.

BETSY Rosie? I know a dozen Rosies I do. Rosie Trilling, she was here. Got her this job myself, I did. Spoke up for her when they wanted a cook. She's gone down in the world, Rosie Trilling has. Nice job she had here, and now she's selling whelks for her grandfather. All because of a couple of street kids.

COOK This boy's sisters, they were.

BETSY Were they now? Doesn't seem right, does it? Just for helping people out like that. Your sisters were they? Didn't look like street kids to me. She was a fine woman, your ma, so Rosie said.

JIM What happened to Emily and Lizzie?

BETSY Don't ask me that, because I don't know the answer. If you wants to climb on the cart I'll take you to your Rosie. But where the girls is, I don't know, and that's the truth.

COOK Don't you dare come back. There's nothing we can do for you. Here, take this bread for your breakfast. God bless you, child. I hope He takes care of you.

Lame Betsy and Jim leave. Cook is joined at the door by Polly. They wave their hands, then Cook closes the door.

Scene Three

*Rosie's cottage, one of a row of cottages next to the Thames. Furnished with crates and boxes. **Rosie** is cooking fish over the fire. **Grandmother** is sitting on a crate, hunched up in a black shawl. **Rosie** feeds her by picking off bits of fish and putting them into her mouth.*

ROSIE Don't gobble it, Grandmother. You'll choke on the bones.

GRANDMOTHER Hungry, that's why.

ROSIE I know you're hungry. You're greedy, too. And you can take your eyes off that tray of whelks. It's all I've got to sell today.

JIM *(calls from the open doorway)* Rosie?

ROSIE The men have set off, son. They left with the tide an hour ago.

JIM Rosie.

ROSIE Yes, I'm Rosie. And I told you…

JIM I've come about Lizzie and Emily. I'm Jim.

ROSIE Lord bless us. Annie Jarvis's little boy?

JIM *(nods)* Ma died. A long time ago. In the Infirmary.

ROSIE Oh, I'm sorry to hear that. I'm sorry.

JIM I ran away because I wanted to tell Lizzie and Emily. I didn't cry, Rosie. I wouldn't cry in that place.

ROSIE Come here, child.

*Rosie puts her arms round him. **Jim** sobs.*

ROSIE There there. You can cry now. You can cry.

JIM *(sobbing and slowly recovering)* Don't send me back there, will you? Can I stay here with you?

ROSIE Stay here? Oh Jim, I don't know. I'll have to hide you somehow. Grandfather would throw you to the gulls, and me with you, if he thought you were intending to stay. Do you understand?

JIM I've been looking for you for days and days. Please don't send me away.

ROSIE You can sleep out there in the boat-shed tonight, if you promise to be careful. It's cold, and it don't half stink with all that rot on the river, but it's dry enough.

JIM I'd like that. I can pretend I'm on a boat.

ROSIE So you can. Like to sail away, would you, Jim? I know I would. Far away to somewhere else.

GRANDMOTHER I'm hungry. Where's my fish?

ROSIE You'll have to share it with the boy, Grandmother. There, that's worried her, greedy old crow. Anywhere would be better than this, Jim. Drowning would be better than this. Don't you ever let Grandfather know you're here. See?

JIM I won't. Rosie? Can't you go back to work at his lordship's house?

ROSIE I wish I could! I was very comfortable there. I was very lucky to get that job. But never mind. I lost it, and that's that.

JIM Was it because of Lizzie and Emily that you lost it?

ROSIE Lord, no. Whatever made you think that? It was because my cooking was so bad! I've never cooked anything but fish in my life! And they expected me to bake bread. Bread! My bread broke the flagstones if I dropped it.

JIM But what about Emily and Lizzie? They didn't get sent to the workhouse, did they?

ROSIE To the workhouse? Emily and Lizzie? I'd have fought them all, his lordship included, if they'd done that to them. No, I'll tell you what happened to Emily and Lizzie. Close your eyes and I'll tell you what happened.

Song/music.

There was a beautiful lady with grey eyes. She came to the Big House, and when she saw Emily and Lizzie she had them washed in her own room, with all lovely soaps and powders and the like. And she sent out for dresses for them, a blue one for Emily, and a white one for Lizzie. And then she took them in a carriage, a beautiful carriage drawn by four white horses. You should have seen them setting off, as proud as little queens! They went all the way to the countryside, to her summer home, to be looked after there.

Jim is asleep.

ROSIE *(sighs)* I wish it was true. Oh yes. I wish it was. Now then, you sleep good and proper, young Jim. When you wakes up you can come to work with me. You'll have to keep moving, same as me. If the bobbies see us standing about we'll both be packed off. We'll be running all day, and no mistake.

Scene Four

A busy street. **Barrow boys** *and* **girls** *selling their wares. Various cries/songs of: 'Flowers! Pretty flowers!', 'Hens for sale! Eggs three a penny!', 'Milko! Creamo!'* (**Lame Betsy**); *'Morning coffee, piping hot!'* (**Maudie**); *'Laces. Who'll buy my laces?'* (**Shrimps**). *Rosie and Jim enter. Rosie has a tray of shrimps etc. strapped to her.*

ROSIE AND JIM *(both shouting)* Whelkso! Salmon for sale! Pickled fish and shrimpso!

Jim dances round her, shyly at first, then more extravagantly as he sees people are watching. **Street children**, *among them* **Shrimps**, *and* **shoppers** *laugh and clap.*

POSH LADY I'll have another bag of shrimps if the boy will dance for me again!

Jim dances again and with a flourish hands her a bag of whelks.

POSH LADY So delightful. I'll come again tomorrow, and bring my friends. They'll be so amused!

*She pays **Rosie** and goes. Other people gather round and buy from **Rosie**.*

SHRIMPS *(imitating the posh lady)* Oh do skip for me, young man. *So* delightful.

JIM Buy some shrimps and I will!

SHRIMPS Buy some shrimps, he says! What with? Anyway, I *am* Shrimps! How can I buy meself, bruvver?

ROSIE I'm very pleased with you, Skipping Jim. I'm selling more salmon than I can pickle. They'll have to have it boiled plain if they want more, and like it! And the whelks and shrimps are going like hot cakes.

BETSY *(approaching)* Rosie! Rosie Trilling!

ROSIE Look Jim, it's Lame Betsy.

JIM Maybe she's found Emily and Lizzie.

ROSIE I don't think so. They're too far away.

BETSY I've been worrying myself soft about this boy. Whether he'd find you, and whether you could give him a home, and how he was doing.

ROSIE He's doing fine. He's a real little dancing man, ain't you, Jim? But he can't stay with me for long, he knows that. I've got him hidden in the boat-shed but I'm in mortal fear of my grandfather finding him and throwing us both out. You know what he's like, Betsy.

BETSY Well, I've got a fine plan! There's a man round the next street, is teaching poor children for nothing. You come with me, Jim. I'm going to take you to school!

JIM No, not school, Betsy. I hate school! I hate schoolteachers!

BETSY He's not a schoolteacher. He's a doctor, so he says. Doctor Barnio or summat. And he's got a school going for the likes of you. He's a queer soul, they say. He comes riding on a donkey, and he stands on a box in the middle of the street and asks people to bring their children along to his school, and he don't charge them nothing! Come on Jim! It's a fine chance for you!

JIM But I want to help Rosie.

ROSIE You go with Betsy. She's right. You ought to be at school.

*Betsy pulls Jim along with her to where a **crowd** is gathered.*

BETSY You'll hear Bible stories, I should think, and sing lots of nice hymns. I don't want you getting into bad ways, Jim, just because you ain't got a mother and father. Look at that crowd! That's Doctor Barnio, talking now.

*Betsy pushes Jim to the front of the **crowd**. **Barnardo**, a thin man with spectacles and fluffy side-whiskers, is standing on a box, turning from side to side. He speaks in a light, soft voice with an Irish accent. The watchers are laughing and jeering.*

BARNARDO Bring your children to me and I will teach them the word of the Lord.

MAN *(in crowd)* Oh yes? And what word might that be? Food?

Crowd laugh.

BARNARDO The message is very simple. This is what I will teach your children – I will teach them that God is love. I will teach them that God is good.

JIM No he ain't! He ain't been good to me!

Everybody laughs.

MAN *(in crowd)* The boy's right! There's not much love around here.

WOMAN *(in crowd)* Clear off! We've heard enough of your soft talk.

*A boy (**Davey**) picks up a lump of mud and flings it at **Barnardo**. He coughs and wipes his mouth on his sleeve. He is jostled off his crate, and as he pushes his way through the crowd he passes **Jim**. He pauses and looks at him with sadness, then goes.*

BETSY *(to Jim)* Go on! Back to your Rosie, you vagabond! There's not much you don't know, after all!

The crowd disperses, except for the street children, Shrimps, Davey, Billy, etc.

DAVEY Hey, there's Skipping Jim!

BILLY Come on, Skipping Jim. Dance for us!

Jim capers round to make them laugh. Rosie joins them.

ROSIE You'll soon wear those boots out. Save your dancing for the proper customers.

Shrimps dances with Jim, imitating him in a clownish way. Several people gather round, laughing, buying from Rosie.

ROSIE I'm going back to the cottage to get some more. I've never sold two whole trayfuls like that in one day, never. You should go on the shows, you two! You should join a travelling circus!

Rosie leaves with Jim, followed by children begging.

DAVEY Give us some, Rosie! Just a couple.

BILLY Have you got any scraps to spare?

Shrimps is alone on stage.

SHRIMPS Wore me out, all that dancing. He's a right one, that Jim is. Now, what've I got? *(empties his pockets)* Enough to get a few more laces to sell and a hot stew from the ale house. Not enough for me lodgings though. Sleep while you can, Shrimps. While there's no bobbies about. Might be snowing tonight, and there'll be no sleeping then, not out here. *(he yawns and falls asleep)*

A poor woman (Muvver) enters.

MUVVER Gotcha! You bin hiding from me, aincha? Where's yer money?

SHRIMPS *(wakes)* Ain't got none.

Muvver tips him over and a coin rolls out of his pocket. She pounces on it. Jim runs in and pauses, watching.

MUVVER Now you've got none!

SHRIMPS Give it back. It's all I've got, that is.

MUVVER Ought to work harder then, instead of sleeping in the daytime.

Muvver laughs and runs off.

JIM *(handing Shrimps a paper bag)* Here, Rosie sent these for you. She said it'll save you pinching them off her.

SHRIMPS Aw, thanks bruvver. Shrimps! I love shrimps, I do. But I've never pinched none off Rosie's stall, never.

JIM You wouldn't dare. She'd pickle you if you did.

SHRIMPS I dare do anyfink, I do. But Rosie, she's like me. She ain't got no more money than me, she ain't. She knows I love shrimps though. Real kind of her, this is.

JIM Are you really called Shrimps?

SHRIMPS Shrimps is what they call me, and Shrimps'll do.

JIM Who was that woman?

SHRIMPS That woman what pinched me profit? Muvver, that was. Me luvvin muvver. Only she kicked me out years ago, didn't she? She only comes looking for me when she wants money for gin. Not much of a muvver, she ain't.

JIM Where d'you live then?

SHRIMPS Depends, don't it? See, if I makes more than a copper or two selling laces, I saves it to spend on a lodging house for the night. I go there about once a month, probly.

JIM Cor. On your own?

SHRIMPS On me own and wiv about fifty other geysers wot snore their heads off all night! It's like a funder-storm sometimes! And if I don't have no money, I sleeps where I can, don't I? Where the bobbies won't find me, that's where I sleep. I spent a week in that place you come from.

JIM What, in the workhouse?

SHRIMPS Worse'n anyfink I ever knowed, that workhouse was. Worse'n sleeping in a barn full of rats, and I done that a time or two.

JIM *(giggling)* Worse than that. Worse than sleeping in a sack full of eels.

SHRIMPS Eels! Eels is charming company. I ate an eel once, when it were still alive. It wriggled all done my throat and round my belly and up again and out through my mouth! 'Bellies!', said the eel. 'Boy's bellies is nearly as bad as the workhouse!' And it wriggled off home. It was all right, that eel.

Both boys are laughing.

SHRIMPS You got a bruvver, Skippin' Jim?

JIM No. Have you?

SHRIMPS Used to have. But I ain't got one now. I'd like a bruvver to go round wiv.

JIM So would I.

*Night watchman **Samuel** trudges past.*

SAMUEL Five of the clock. Five o'clock, my lovelies!

SHRIMPS Got to go. I got a queue to see to. People often breaks their bootlaces when they're standing in queues. Just snaps off, they do, if I crawls round and tweaks 'em when they ain't looking.

JIM Will you be here tomorrow?

***Shrimps** takes a bunch of laces out of his pocket and swirls them round his head, doing his dancing imitation of **Jim**. Then he runs off.*

JIM Be nice to have a bruvver. A bruvver like Shrimps. Real nice, that would be. What would Rosie say, if I took Shrimps to her boat-shed? Here's my bruvver, I'd tell her. Can he stay here, Rosie? And she'd say, welcome! Any bruvver of Jim's is welcome here.

Grandfather and Grimy Nick come towards him.

GRANDFATHER Bless my soul, if it ain't the boy I was telling yer about, Mister Grimes. Know me, don't yer, lad? *(twisting Jim's ear)*

JIM No mister, I don't.

GRANDFATHER Well, I know you. You're the little rat what's been skulking in my boat-shed. Don't think I don't know what Rosie's been up to. I'll weasel him out, I thought to myself. I'll winkle him out when the time is right.

JIM Please mister. Let me stay there. I ain't doin' no harm.

GRANDFATHER Oh, I got better plans for you. You ought to be grateful, boy. Grateful instead of whining.

GRIMY NICK Stand up straight, boy. Let's have a look at you. No. He's no good. He's only a twig. There's no bones in him, hardly.

GRANDFATHER He'll grow. I know his type. He'll grow big and powerful. You can train him up, Nick, when he's only that big. Won't give you no trouble, that size. He's just right. And while he's training, he won't eat much.

GRIMY NICK Well, he's here, and I'm stuck for a boy, so I'll take him. *(he tosses Grandfather a coin)*

GRIMY NICK Come on, boy.

GRANDFATHER Go on. You go with Grimy Nick. You heard. I've got you a job.

JIM Can't I just tell Rosie?

GRANDFATHER She won't need no telling. I'll thank her, shall I, for stealing food from her grandmother's mouth to stuff in yours?

Go on. Go with Grimy Nick. You've got a home and a job now. You've nothing more to want in life, that's what.

Scene Five

*The Wharf. A large warehouse, BEST COALS OF COCKERILL AND CO. In front is moored a coal lighter (barge) 'The Lily'. A gloomy man, **Mr Cockerill**, is sweeping the wharf yard.*

COCKERILL Thought you weren't coming no more.

GRIMY NICK Damn you. You'd think the worst of the Angel Gabriel, you would. Get on board, boy, don't stand idle.

A dog is heard growling (offstage).

GRIMY NICK That's Snipe. He's down there in the hold of the boat. See him? Now he's smelled yer, he'll never forget yer. Never. He'll know you belong on here, see?

JIM *(afraid)* Yes, mister.

GRIMY NICK Which means that if yer tries to run away, he'll be after yer, and he'll probly eat yer alive. The faster yer runs, the faster he runs. See? So yer'd better not try. He's quite friendly. Just so long as you're friendly to me. See?

Jim nods, backing away from the growls (offstage).

GRIMY NICK Well, we'll get along very well, in that case. Now, get on that boat and start shovelling.

COCKERILL Don't tell me you're ready! If we don't get this load out we'll have lost next Saturday's tide, never mind this one.

GRIMY NICK I knows that. I've been training my new boy. Go on boy, get on with it! Shovel this coal up, and be quick about it. It'll take us three days to shift this lot onto the wharf, and then we goes out for more, off one of them big boats. So don't think yer work's done. Yer work's never done. Not while there's coal in the ground.

Jim tries to shovel coal out of the boat onto the wharf, but is too weak.

GRIMY NICK Curse you boy! Not like that, you idle pup! Work harder! Harder!

*Mime of the two shovelling, **Jim** panting and weak, **Nick** swift and strong, a dance of lifting and tipping, with **Cockerill** looking on, shadows swinging in lantern light to a grunting, weary rhythm.*

GRIMY NICK Work! Shovel! Shovel! Work! Lift! Swing! Over! Down! Lift! Swing! Over! Down!

COCKERILL *(joins in)* Work! Shovel! Shovel! Work!

*When **Jim** stops to rest, **Grimy Nick** swings the flat of his shovel across **Jim's** back. At last the work stops.*

GRIMY NICK Yer only a bundle of sticks, but yer've worked. If yer wants a bowl of mutton stew come with me to the ale-house, and I'll see yer set up.

Scene Six

*The Waterman's Arms. A dark, noisy ale-house with a low blackened ceiling and lanterns hanging from the beams, thick with smoke from the fire in the hearth. **Men** and **women** stand round puffing at pipes and drinking ale. A row of field children, (**Minnie**, **Kitty**, **Alfie** etc.) roped together, stand at the doorway. A **man** stands up to go. **Minnie** touches his arm.*

MINNIE Want any field workers, mister?

*The **man** shakes his head and leaves. The **children** sink down, disappointed.*

KITTY Here, Grimy Nick's got another boy.

MINNIE Wouldn't be him, I wouldn't. Wouldn't work for Grimy Nick, even if he paid me a shilling a day!

*Grimy Nick enters with **Jim**.*

44

GRIMY NICK Clear away, you scruffy bunch. This is my midget, little Jim. Show 'em your muscles, little Jim! Didn't know 'e 'ad any, till he came to work alongside of me. *(he pats **Jim's** head in a fatherly sort of way)* Find yourself a stool by the door and keep quiet. Barmaid! A bowl of stew and a small draught of ale for the boy. And a big quart pot for me. I could drink the river dry tonight.

SILAS You wouldn't know the difference, her ale's got so much water in it!

BARMAID *(laughs)* None of your cheek, old Silas. Here y'are boy. Eat up. Best mutton stew tonight. This'll stick to your ribs and make you fat.

*Jim is surrounded by the **field children**.*

MINNIE You with Grimy Nick?

JIM What if I am?

KITTY His last boy was took to ospickal, beat to bits, wasn't he Minnie?

MINNIE That's right, he was. Poor old Benjamin.

JIM Won't beat me. I'll beat him first.

ALFIE Give us a sip of your ale.

JIM Don't take too much. I've been swallowing nothing but coal dust for three days.

MINNIE Give us a spoonful of stew, Nick's boy.

JIM Won't your master get you any?

ALFIE We ain't got a master now. Old Silas has just finished with us.

MINNIE We worked his fields for a month, see, and now we have to find someone else. That's why we're waiting here.

KITTY Been here four days now.

JIM Cor. I suppose I'm lucky then. Least I've got a job.

Alfie Not with Grimy Nick, you ain't lucky. You wait till he gets drunk. You'll have to watch out for yourself then.

Grimy Nick *(staggers out, slightly drunk)* Jim, you blockhead, it's time for you to take me home. Don't run off. I need your shoulder to lean on. Move! Tide's turning! If we miss this tide, boy, we'll lose our coal cargo to another lighterman. And if that happens, I'll beat you till you're black and blue. Get moving. We're sailing tonight!

Scene Seven

On board 'The Lily', which is out on the estuary, and tied up to a big boat, 'The Queen of the North'.

Grimy Nick Right. See that big boat alongside of us? She's 'Queen of the North', she is. She's brought a cargo of coals out, and we has to load them off her and take 'em back to shore, over to Cockerill's. When the ship lowers her coal down, swing the basket round and tip it into the hold. Look smart. Let's watch yer doing it.

Jim does so, choking with the coal dust.

Grimy Nick That's your job for today, and tomorrow, till we get the hold full. We've got eighty tons to load, and the quicker we gets it done, the quicker we gets back to Cockerill's. See we don't lose any coals overboard. And keep the dog out of the way. And keep moving.

Dance movement begins again, this time an upward stretching as if reaching for the swinging basket, tipping it out, and shovelling the coal.

Grimy Nick Swing! Tip! Shovel! Swing! Tip! Shovel! Swing! Tip! Shovel!

Jim staggers back, exhausted.

Grimy Nick That'll do. Me belly's growling for food. Put some hatch boards across. I'm going aboard the big ship for some food.

You keep that stove going or I'll wipe your brains away.

Nick climbs a rope ladder that take him on to 'Queen of the North'. Jim squats by the pot stove, warming his hands.

JIM Hope he brings me something nice and tasty. Could do with one of Rosie's herrings now, or a bit of stew, all hot and steamy. Anything'll do. Hope it's tasty, though.

JOSH *(off)* Hey below! Coming down!

A man, Josh, climbs down the ladder from the big boat. He jumps down onto 'The Lily'. Jim holds up the lantern.

JIM Master's not here. What do you want?

JOSH Come to see how Benjamin is.

JIM I don't know any Benjamin.

JOSH The other lad that comes with Nick. Big, clumsy lad.

JIM Oh, Benjamin. I've heard of him, yes. Some field children told me about him. I think he might be in hospital.

JOSH Well, I'm not surprised. He looked bad last time I saw him. All skin and bones. Walked like a little old man. I've been worrying about him. And I'd say it was Nick that got him that way.

JIM I don't know anything about it.

JOSH Beats you too, does he?

JIM Yes, mister.

JOSH Think they own you, some of these masters. Think they own you, body and soul. But they don't. Not your soul. Know what your soul is?

JIM No, mister.

JOSH Well, it comes with you when you're born, and it's yours to keep. It's like your name. And my name's Josh, and I don't mind telling you that for nothing. You've got a good stove going there. I'd be quite pleased to spend the night here, where it's quiet.

JIM I think Nick's coming down soon with some food for me.

JOSH Nick's fast asleep on my ship. He's stuffed his belly so full that he can't stuff any more in it. So don't expect him down for a bit. Not till the tide comes back in, I'd say.

JIM Where does the tide go to?

JOSH Go to? Well, it's just there, isn't it? It's pulled over one way, then it's pulled over another, but it just keeps coming in and out, day after day after day, and it always will. Where there isn't land there's water, lots of it. And you can only see the top of it. There's more of it underneath. Miles and miles of it. Imagine that!

JIM So I wouldn't be able to touch the bottom if I jumped in?

JOSH Not unless you can swim like a fish. I advise you to stay on board and keep your skin dry.

JIM Do you live in that big boat?

JOSH No more than I can help. I've got a proper home. As soon as you lighters take our coal off us we go home. We sail up the coast of England from here, right up to the north. And that's not the end of the sea, you know. If you just stayed on water you could go right round the world.

JIM I wish I could do that.

JOSH You're a funny one, you are. What would you want to do that for? It's big and empty, the sea is. Lonely.

JIM I might find somewhere nice to live.

JOSH You don't like living here, then?

JIM No mister, I don't. It's cold and it's hard and I don't get enough food. And he shouts and screams so much. And hits me till I'm covered in bruises.

JOSH Not much of a life for a boy. I've got a little lad like you. I'm glad he's tucked up in bed with his sisters and his mam, and not stuck out here. Have you got a mother and father somewhere?

JIM No mister. I've only got Grimy Nick.

Josh I'm sorry to hear that. Well, I'll be getting up on deck for some sleep. We'll be off with tomorrow's tide.

Jim Josh. Can I come with you?

Josh Come with me? Why?

Jim I think it would be better, that's all.

Josh Nothing gets much better. Not till you're dead. *(he goes)*

Jim Nothing here. Nothing. Only the sea, and the black boats bobbing, and the lanterns glowing on the water like little yellow faces. Not a sound, Jim. Even Snipe is down in his hold, fast asleep for once. Lonely, it is. I wish I'd got a brother. I wish I'd got a brother. *(shouts)* I wish I'd got a brother! *(then, in Shrimp's voice)* You got lots of bruvvers, Jim. Only they ain't around at the moment, is all.

He pulls his sack round him and falls asleep. Light comes up. **Grimy Nick** *climbs on board, belching and singing loudly. He throws scraps down the hold to the dog.*

Grimy Nick Here y'are, Snipe. Bit of supper like I promised.

Snipe *growls, offstage.* **Jim** *starts up and holds out his hands for food.*

Grimy Nick What you looking at me like that for? Can't you feel the boat moving? That's the tide turning. *(hits him)* The tide! D'you hear me? There's work to do, such as you've never seen before, so look lively and get the boat ready, and wake me when you've done.

Grimy Nick *rolls himself in a blanket, snoring.*

Jim *(to himself, in **Shrimps's** voice)* Tell him, bruvver. He's forgot you. Tell him! Nick. Did you forget my food?

Grimy Nick *(angry)* What's that? What d'yer want?

Jim My supper, Nick. I think you forgot it.

Grimy Nick Forgot, did I?

Jim I think so, Nick.

Grimy Nick There's food for you. Down there. In the dog's mouth!

Scene Eight

Barnardo's study. **Barnardo** *is sitting at his desk,* **Jim** *by the fire, as in Act One, Scene One.*

Barnardo I can hardly believe that anyone could be so cruel to a child, Jim. Did you not try to run away?

Jim I did once. We moored up to a bank in the river one night because the water was choppy and Grimy Nick was feeling sick. And when he was asleep I said to myself, 'You've got to do it, Jim'. I nipped over the side of the boat as quick as a rat.

Barnardo Good for you. And what happened?

Jim Snipe heard me, didn't he? He came howling and barking after me and nearly tore me leg off, and Grimy Nick woke up and came after me.

Music/sounds of howling and barking.

Grimy Nick *(lit, standing front of stage with rope in his hands)* Try to run away, would you? Leave me stranded with no-one to help me? Is that what I get for all my kindness? Well, it won't happen again, see? One end of this rope is going round the mast, and the other end is going round your neck. You're lucky Snipe didn't rip you to bits. Grimy Nick saved your life. Remember that. *(Nick's light goes off)*

Jim *(to Barnardo)* But later on, I saved *his* life.

Barnardo You saved Grimy Nick's life? Tell me about that.

Jim We were loading the coal into baskets at Cockerill's wharf. They had to be lifted right up high over our heads, and I saw that one of them had a rope that was fraying. It was right over Grimy Nick's head! I yelled to him, 'Nick, Nick, look out!' He dodged out of the way, just in time, but he was knocked out.

Grimy Nick *is lying on the floor at front of stage, lit.* ***Cockerill*** *runs on.*

COCKERILL By God, he's out cold! He's gone and died. *(**Nick** groans)* No he ain't! He's coming alive again!

GRIMY NICK Feels like the whole world has fell on top of me.

COCKERILL You could have been buried alive. You'd have been dead and gone proper, if it hadn't been for your boy here.

GRIMY NICK My boy?

COCKERILL Saved your life.

GRIMY NICK Saved my life? *(starts sobbing)* What did he go and do that for? *(**Nick's** lights off)*

BARNARDO So, I should think Grimy Nick was a bit kinder to you after that?

JIM No, mister. He was just as bad as ever. Still kept me tied up. It was back to shovelling and sweeping, piling coal onto the lighter, piling it off at the wharf, backwards and forwards to the big boats, but I never saw that man Josh again. He took a job on shore, they said, to be near his wife and his littl'uns. It was dreary. And then the circus came! You should have seen it, mister Barnie! You should have seen them, all marching on the river bank!

Scene Nine

Circus music. A circus procession marches past: ***jugglers****,* ***tumblers****,* ***clowns*** *carrying a banner saying, 'Juglini's Champion Circus'.* ***Jim*** *and* ***Grimy Nick*** *are watching from 'The Lily'.*

CLOWNS *(variously)* Roll up! Roll up for the greatest show on earth! Roll up to Juglini's Champion Circus! See the strongest man in the universe! See the Flying Lady! See the Dancing Horses! Roll up! Roll up!

Juglini *and* ***Madame Juglini*** *and their children,* ***Maria*** *and* ***Antonio****, bring up the rear.*

Maria Look, there's a boy on that boat, tied up like a dog.

Madame Juglini He must be wicked, then.

Antonio He doesn't look wicked. He just looks dirty.

*He stands on his hands and waggles his feet at **Jim**. **Jim** laughs and waves. **Antonio** stands up and waves at **Jim**.*

Antonio *(calls)* Come to the circus! Come to the circus!

Jim *(calls back)* I will! I will! *(to himself, in **Shrimps's** voice)* See. Another bruvver, Jim. They're all over the place, ain't they?

Grimy Nick Want to go pageanting, do you?

Jim Please, Nick. Can I?

Grimy Nick *(laughs)* Pageanting's for fools and time-wasters. *(hits **Jim**)* Does that answer your question? *(he goes)*

Jim What am I doing here, tied up like an animal, eating and sleeping like an animal? Time to go, Jim. Time to skip off, and no mistake.

Scene Ten

Barnardo's study.

Jim And this time I did it right. I got a sharp bit of coal, and I rubbed at the rope till I cut it free. Then I tied Snipe up with it. When Nick came home, dead drunk as usual, I tripped him up so he fell down the hold. Then I put the hatch cover over and piled heavy coals on top so he wouldn't be able to push it up.

Barks and muffled bangs and shouts of fury in echo offstage.

Jim *(front of stage)* Then I ran for it. I ran like the clappers! I got away!

ACT THREE
Scene One

The circus field. The big tent is being put up by several men, encouraged by **Juglini**. *Behind it are circus caravans, all painted in bright colours with the words 'Juglini's Champion Circus'. Juglini's van has a green door with a brass knocker, and cabin windows with muslin curtains, and a funnel at the back with smoke curling from it.* **Jim** *sits by it, looking at it longingly.*

JIM Imagine living in that little caravan, Jim. All bright and cosy and warm. Imagine living anywhere. It'll be prison you'll be living in, when the bobbies catch you. You've done it now. You've left your master to suffocate, and you've strangled his dog on the rope. You've killed them both, you have. Now you're for it, Jim. What to do? Got to eat first, that's what. Eat, and then think.

Madame Juglini opens the door of the caravan. **Antonio** *and* **Maria** *squirm onto the step in front of her.*

MARIA Who's that dirty boy, Mamma?

MADAME JUGLINI He's a ragamuffin. What do you want, boy?

JIM Please missus. I've come for a job if you'll give me one. I'll help to put the tent up. I'll muck out the horses, and clean 'em up bright and smart. And I don't want money, missus.

MADAME JUGLINI Don't want money? I've never heard that before.

JIM If you'll feed me, missus, I'll do anything.

MARIA He's dirty, Mamma.

MADAME JUGLINI He is. Very dirty. How did you get so dirty?

JIM On 'The Lily' – I don't know.

MARIA *(laughs)* He doesn't know!

ANTONIO You were that boy on the lighter! Tied up!

MARIA Tied up like a dog. Woof, woof!

JIM Not me. That must have been someone else you saw. Please, missus. I'll do anything.

ANTONIO Can we give him some work, Mamma? I think he looks nice.

MADAME JUGLINI We have a busy day. We have a costume to make for the Strongest Man in the Universe. The last Strongest Man ran away with the Flying Lady and took his loincloth with him. I don't suppose you've ever done any sewing, have you?

JIM Yes, in the workhouse – er, no, I mean. No, I don't know if I can sew.

MARIA He doesn't know anything!

JIM But I'll try, missus.

MARIA *(calls)* Papa, look at this dirty boy.

Juglini comes to the caravan. He rubs Jim's hair and a cloud of coal dust flies up. Maria and Antonio back away, coughing.

JUGLINI This is not a boy! This is a sack of coal!

MADAME JUGLINI He says he wants a job, Juglini.

JIM Please, mister.

JUGLINI Now tell me true. Have you run away from home?

JIM I haven't got a home.

MADAME JUGLINI No home?

JIM I used to live on a coal-lighter.

ANTONIO It *was* you! You were on 'The Lily'!

JIM No, not 'The Lily'. Another one. 'Rosie', it was called. I... I think the lighterman might have died, sir. I think he might have got trapped. It was... I... I haven't got anywhere to live now.

Juglini and Madame Juglini exchange glances.

Antonio Give him a job with me, Papa! He's funny!

Juglini We have jobs he can do, yes.

Jim Thanks, mister. Oh Mister Juglini, thank you!

Juglini Give him some breakfast, Madame Juglini. This sack of coal is empty.

Madame Juglini He can jump in the stream first and wash himself before he sets foot in my caravan. Go on boy. Antonio will show you.

Antonio and Jim run off.

Juglini Then he can whiten the harnesses with Antonio. There's a job. Let's see how well he does that. Keep him busy, Madame Juglini. And don't lose sight of him.

Madame Juglini What is this? You have a soft heart for a dirty ragamuffin?

Juglini Just do as I say. When the people turn up for the show tonight, he can help Antonio take money on the door.

Madame Juglini Can we trust a boy like this with money?

Juglini Keep him here, Madame Juglini. I have a visit to make, and some questions to ask.

Madame Juglini Visit? On circus day? Where are you going, Juglini?

Juglini To the river bank. But say nothing to the boy. I will be back long before the show begins. *(he goes)*

Madame Juglini Maria, your papa has gone mad. He goes to walk by the river, and we don't even have a loincloth yet for the strongest man in the world. To work, child. To work!

They go inside the caravan.

Scene Two

*Outside the circus tent. Bright lanterns hang from trees. Sound of a circus band. The **clowns** and **jugglers** parade on. **Antonio** and **Jim** follow, banging drums. **Jim** is dancing. **Maria** runs on stage.*

MARIA The people are coming, the people are coming!

MADAME JUGLINI *(shouting at door of tent)* Roll up! Roll up, for the greatest show on earth! See the Dancing Horses of Arabie! See Madame Bombadini as she flies through the air! See the strongest man in the Universe! Roll up! Roll up!

ANTONIO Can you count, Jim?

JIM No. No-one taught me counting.

ANTONIO Don't worry. I'll teach you. But tonight, I'll take the money and you give the tickets out. What you grinning at?

JIM Nuffin. I'm just happy. Everything's all right now. And tonight I'm going to sleep in your little green caravan, and I never dreamed of anything so pretty. Tomorrow I'll brush the horses again, and bang the drum, and help with the tickets, and you'll teach me to count! Everything's all right now.

ANTONIO Course it is, Jim. We'll look after you.

JIM Your Ma and Pa are very kind to me. They treat me like – well, like I was in the family.

ANTONIO Wait till they see you dancing! They'll put you in a clown's costume and give you a job in the ring!

JIM *(dances around with happiness)* Will they? This is my best day, Antonio. My best day ever! Roll up! Roll up! Hooray for Juglini's circus! The greatest show on earth!

*****Families** come in, talking and laughing. **Antonio** takes the money and **Jim** gives them tickets.*

JIM Here you are, mister. Here you are, missus.

ANTONIO No, Jim. Sir, it is, not mister. And madame.

JIM Oh, right. Here you are, mister sir. Here you are, missus madame. Enjoy the show.

*Grimy Nick enters, limping, with **Juglini**.*

GRIMY NICK Show me where he is. I'll murder him.

JUGLINI In a moment, in a moment.

GRIMY NICK Let me get at him. I'll break his neck, I will.

JUGLINI *(holding **Nick** back)* My reward first, if you please.

MADAME JUGLINI If you please.

*Madame Juglini holds out her hand. Grumbling, **Nick** tosses her a coin. At that moment, **Jim** sees **Nick**.*

JIM Oh no! He's here!

ANTONIO What's the matter?

JIM It's Nick! It's the man I killed! I gotta go. Help me get out. Help me!

***Nick** sees **Jim**, roars and plunges towards him.*

NICK That's the boy! Come over here. Stop him someone. I'll beat the living daylights out of him. Stop him!

***Jim** dodges away. **Antonio** runs forward and stumbles in front of **Nick** so **Nick** trips over him. **Jim** runs off.*

JIM *(calling)* Bye, bruvver! Bye!

Scene Three

*A lane, moonlight. A signpost saying 'London 30 miles'. **Jim** comes on, running slowly, very tired.*

98

JIM It's so big and lonely here. I've run so far, surely Nick won't find me now. Stop and sleep, that's what I'd like to do. Stop running, Jim, and sleep. But I daren't, not out in the open like this. He might find me, and if he does, he'll cut my throat. A barn would do fine. A barn full of rats, even. *(in Shrimps's voice)* I'd rather sleep in a barn full of rats, and I've done that a time or two. Well, rats is charming company, bruvver. At least they knows where it's warm and dry. *(own voice)* Keep going, bruvver. This must lead somewhere.

*A **beggar** jumps out and grabs **Jim** from behind.*

JIM Don't kill me, Nick. Please don't kill me.

BEGGAR I ain't no murderer. I'm looking for bread, that's all. You got bread?

JIM No. I ain't got nothing.

BEGGAR You're no good to me, then. Off you go.

JIM Mister. What does this sign say?

BEGGAR Can't you read?

JIM No.

BEGGAR Neither can I, boy. But my feet can tell you what it says, cos I've just come from there. Two or three days ago. London town, it says. Two days' walking. No bread there, neither.

He stumps off, whistling.

JIM London! Rosie lives in London Town, Jim! You're going home! Home!

Scene Four

*London, the area near Rosie's house. Men are digging and building, whistling and bustling. **Lame Betsy** is standing watching, her arms folded, a shawl over her shoulders. She hardly takes her eyes off the workmen during the whole scene. **Jim** walks on, weary.*

JIM This isn't right. Rosie's house should be here, but it's not. It's gone. You're Betsy, aren't you? Betsy?

BETSY Do I know you?

JIM It's Jim. Skipping Jim.

BETSY Skipping Jim? No. Don't remember no-one of that name.

JIM What's happening round here? Everything's changed.

BETSY They're building a big new dock here, for all the boats. Wunnerful, ain't it! Wunnerful. They say there's more than two thousand men working here. Fancy! I never knew there was two thousand men in the whole world!

JIM But what happened to all the houses? And all the people who lived here? Where's Rosie?

BETSY Rosie? I know a dozen Rosies, and they've all lost their homes now. Don't know where any of the Rosies have gone. Pastures new, I hope!

Betsy wanders off, laughing.

JIM You're on your own now, bruvver, and no mistake. You ain't got no-one.

WOMAN HAWKER Shrimpso! Whelkso!

JIM Rosie! It's me, Jim! Wait for me.

WOMAN HAWKER *(turns)* What d'you want?

JIM Oh. I thought you were Rosie.

WOMAN HAWKER Well I ain't, so you can clear off home.

JIM I ain't got one. Can I help you?

WOMAN HAWKER Help me? What can you do to help me?

JIM I could dance for you, and shout out 'Shrimpso! Whelkso!' I used to do it for Rosie. It would bring all the people round to buy from you.

WOMAN HAWKER And as soon as they come, you'd pick their pockets and we'd both be done for it. Not likely. Clear off.

*Street boys **Billy** and **Davey** and others gather round, holding out their hands to the **woman hawker**.*

STREET BOYS *(whining)* Give us some shrimps, lady!

WOMAN HAWKER Clear off, varmints! Shrimpso! Whelkso!

Jim skips round her, a little helpless tired dance.

JIM Look. This is what I do.

*The **woman hawker** shakes her head at him and walks away.*

JIM *(to himself)* No wonder she don't want me. Can't dance no more, Jim. My leg hurts where Snipe nearly bit it off. And my boots is full of holes. Lizzie's boots, they are. Can't throw them away, even though they lets all the weather in.

BILLY Here, you remind me of Skippin' Jim. He used to come round here, long time ago.

JIM You don't know a boy called Shrimps, do you?

BILLY Course I do!

DAVEY Everyone knows Shrimps.

JIM Know where he is?

BILLY Under a fruit cart round the back of the market. He's not well enough to sleep up on the rooftops like us. Follow me, only don't let nobody see.

Scene Five

*The market area. **Samuel** the watchman is sleeping by his brazier. There are some heaped-up boxes. **Billy** and **Davey** lead **Jim** round the workmen to a cart where **Shrimps** lies like a bundle of rags.*

BILLY *(softly)* Look, under this cart. Here's Shrimps. Only he's badly now. Awful badly. *(he takes an apple and a bit of bread out of his cap)* Here y'are, Shrimps. Some bits to eat and that, like I promised. Only I can't stop, there's work to do. But someone's come to see you.

Billy motions to Jim to take his place and he and Davey run off.

JIM Shrimps? It's Skipping Jim. Remember? Your bruvver, Shrimps! It's me!

SHRIMPS Used to have a bruvver. Ages ago. He died or summat. And then there was a boy who danced a lot. He was a kind of bruvver, but he went off somewhere.

JIM That was me! I'm Skipping Jim. You must remember me.

SHRIMPS *(coughs)* I was looking all over for you.

JIM I was sold, Shrimps. A man took me away and treated me awful bad. But I got away. Thought I'd killed him. Hey, are you all right? Here, try and eat this.

Jim breaks the bread and tries to feed Shrimps with it. Shrimps coughs and turns his head away.

SHRIMPS *(weakly)* Fink I swallowed a fly. Must've slept wiv me mouth open.

JIM Soon as you're better we'll go round together, like you said. Like proper bruvvers. Here, sit up and eat this. You gotta eat, Shrimps. What's up with you?

Shrimps struggles to sit up.

SHRIMPS *(weakly)* Old age, bruvver.

JIM What really happened?

SHRIMPS I got beat up, didn't I? This old gentleman give me a guinea, honest he did. Probly thought it was a farthing, but he give me a guinea, fair and square. I think he took a fancy to me charming face. It's true.

Jim I believe you.

Shrimps And I was follered down this alley. Some bloke said I'd nicked it off the old gentleman and I had to give it back. And when I said I hadn't they started kicking me and punching me like I was a doll of straw. But I wasn't going to give me guinea up, was I? It was a present. Sooner give it to me ma than them blokes. So I stuck it under me armpit. Anyway, they must've knocked me out good and proper. When I came round, me jacket had gone and me guinea wiv it, and all me laces, too. So the boys brought me here. Carried me, they did.

Jim You should be in the hospital.

Shrimps *(panicking)* I don't want no ospickal. I don't want no ospickal.

Jim I won't take you there, I promise. Not if you don't want to go. But you're poorly. You're awful poorly. I don't know what to do. Shrimps, you're so cold. Here, I'll lie down by you, keep you warm. You'll be all right, bruvver. I'll look after you now.

Night falls. **Samuel** *wakes, pokes the coal in his brazier and warms his hands by it. He peers under the cart at* **Jim** *and* **Shrimps** *and shakes his head.*

Samuel Sleep well, my lovelies. If I could powder your dreams with blessings, I would. *(he picks up his lantern and goes off, calling)* Half past five and good to be alive! Heaven help us all.

Lights soften to morning. **Maudie** *wheels a cart onstage with a steaming jug of coffee, milk, mugs etc., 'Maudie's Coffee Shop' painted on it.* **People** *are walking past on their way to work.*

Maudie *(calling)* Come and buy. Here's your morning coffee. Piping hot coffee for sale. Best coffee in town.

Jim wakes up. He tries to rouse **Shrimps** *who groans and rolls away, huddled in his sacking.*

Jim Wake up, Shrimps. It's morning.

SHRIMPS Don't want to wake up. Don't want morning.

JIM You're blazing hot. Hotter than Samuel's fire.

MAUDIE Needs a doctor, he does.

JIM He's been like this for days now, since I come to him. I wish I could buy him some medicine. But he won't go to the hospital. I promised him. He's scared of being taken to the workhouse.

MAUDIE Nowhere else for him. 'Cept a pauper's grave, and that'd be a blessing.

JIM Don't say that, Maudie. He'll be all right when I get a bit of money for medicine.

A gentleman enters.

MAUDIE Coffee, sir?

GENTLEMAN Certainly.

JIM I'll ask him, bruvver. Won't do any harm, will it? Please, mister.

GENTLEMAN What is it?

JIM Please, mister. My brother's ever so ill. Please can I have some money for a doctor?

GENTLEMAN Can't I drink coffee without being pestered by beggars?

Gentleman puts his mug back on the cart and walks away.

MAUDIE Now you've lost me my customer. He'd have bought another mug, he would. Don't you dare bother my customers again.

JIM Doesn't anybody care? Shrimps is sick, and nobody cares. I went begging in front of the theatre queue last night. There was ever so many fine people there, all like that gentleman, and they was all rich. But they all looked through me as if I wasn't there when I asked them for money.

MAUDIE Nobody likes beggars. You have to learn that for a start. Sell 'em something, but don't beg.

JIM And then I danced for them, and they all clapped and I thought, now's my chance. 'Can anyone give me the name of a doctor, please?' I asked them. 'One that won't charge money?' And they all turned away as if I was some kind of dirty animal, they did. I don't know what to do. I want to help Shrimps get better, so we can be bruvvers again. He won't die, will he Maudie?

MAUDIE Here, you're done in, ain't you? You won't help your friend that way, not if you go sick too. Have some coffee, warm you up.

JIM Oh, thanks Maudie. Here, Shrimps. Have a little sip. *(he tries to give some to **Shrimps**, who just moans and turns away)* If I could find a doctor, he might let me do jobs for him to pay for the medicine. I'd do anything.

MAUDIE There is a doctor of some sort, not far from here. But I've never heard of him doing any doctoring. Barnie something, they call him. The little kids next door to me go to his school.

JIM School? I don't want anything to do with school.

MAUDIE The Ragged School. Ain't you heard of it? All I know is, it's somewhere kids go when they don't have money to pay for school. They do a lot of praying and hymn singing. Sounds nice.

JIM No. I wouldn't go there, Maudie. Never.

MAUDIE Suit yourself. He's the only doctor I know of. Here, me coffee's going cold, talking to you! *(shouts out, pushing her cart: 'Coffee! Buy your morning coffee here! Piping hot!')*

JIM What do you think, bruvver? School! God is just, God is good, God is holy, God is love. And then they beats you up like you was an animal. No. I hate school, me. I'm not going to school. Please let them take you to the hospital, Shrimps.

SHRIMPS *(weakly)* I'm all right here. Proper little palace, this crate.

*Shrimps starts coughing. **Jim** holds a rag to **Shrimps's** mouth.*

JIM Here, use this rag. That's it. *(looks at the rag)* You go to sleep now. You'll be all right. *(turning away)* Don't die, Shrimps! Hold on, bruvver. Hold on.

Jim runs to Maudie.

JIM Maudie. Maudie!

MAUDIE What now?

JIM Look at this rag, Maudie. He's coughing up blood. That's bad, isn't it? He's getting worse. Can you come to him?

MAUDIE I can't leave my stall. If I don't give breakfast to the early workers I've lost my best trade. You need a doctor for him.

JIM If you tell me where that school is, I'll go there.

MAUDIE It's round about. Over there somewhere. Somewhere round Ernest Street. Ask those children.

Davey and Billy run on, begging Maudie for milk.

DAVEY Hey, Maudie. Give us some coffee.

MAUDIE Be off with you! If I give me coffee to every starving kid, my own will be starving, won't they? Clear off now.

BILLY Some sugar then?

Maudie goes, pushing her cart. Davey pinches a jug of milk as she passes. Maudie sees, and ignores it.

DAVEY How's Shrimps?

JIM Go and see for yourself. Awful bad. Know where the Ragged School is?

DAVEY I've heard of it. There was a man with a donkey used to come round wanting boys to go to his school.

JIM Oh yes! I remember him now.

BILLY We used to chuck tomatoes at him. School! *(he spits)* Don't trust them places, I don't.

DAVEY Here, this is for Shrimps. Present from Maudie. *(he holds out the little jug)*

JIM You give it him. You sit with him for a bit. I got to go somewhere. Tell him I'll be back soon as I can. *(he runs off)*

Scene Six

*The street. Some ragged **children** come out of a shed, clutching slates and singing a hymn loudly and cheerfully. **Dr Barnardo** locks the door behind them.*

BARNARDO Good night, children. Hurry home now.

CHILDREN Good night, teacher.

***Barnardo** exits as **Jim** enters from another direction.*

JIM Do you know where the Ragged School is?

CHILD Yes. We've just been there. It's that donkey shed. Nice and warm it is, in there.

JIM Is there a doctor there?

CHILD 2 Only Doctor Barnio. Only he don't give us medicine, he gives us hymns!

*The **children** start to sing a hymn, laughing.*

CHILD 3 You can't get in. He's not there now. He's just gone home.

JIM Oh no! Which way did he go?

CHILD He's just climbed on that carriage, look.

*The **children** run off, still singing and laughing.*

JIM *(runs)* Dr Barnie! Dr Barnie! Wait, please wait. He's gone. Now I'll have to wait till tomorrow. I'll have to tell Shrimps. Tomorrow I'll ask that Doctor Barnie to help. You'll be all right tomorrow, I'll tell him. I've found a doctor for you, bruvver. *(he runs off)*

66

Scene Seven

The market area. It is dark, except for a small candle or lantern placed next to **Shrimps**. **Samuel** *is sitting nearby.* **Jim** *enters.*

JIM It's going to be all right, Shrimps. Tomorrow. I'll get a doctor and he won't charge nuffin 'cos I'm going to go to his school, see. He'll get you better, and I won't let him send you to hospital. See, it'll be fine. Shrimps? You're cold, Shrimps. Cold as a stone, bruvver.

Jim starts crying silently. **Samuel** *puts his hand on* **Jim's** *shoulder.*

SAMUEL Reckon you'll have to go, Skippin' Jim. They'll be bringing the pauper's cart for Shrimps here soon, an' if they sees you here, you knows where they'll take you.

JIM Pauper's cart, Samuel? What for?

SAMUEL You know what for. 'Cos he's dead, poor soul.

JIM He's asleep, Samuel. That's all. He'll be all right. I'm getting the doctor tomorrow. He'll be all right.

Davey, Billy and others creep in and put scraps of flowers and candles by **Shrimps**, *saying 'Bye Shrimps' softly, then run away again.* **Samuel** *picks up his lantern.*

SAMUEL Five o' clock! Time to get up, my lovelies! Time to get up.

Jim takes off his boots and puts them next to **Shrimps**.

JIM 'Bye, bruvver. I'm on me own again now. Wish we could have gone round together, like you said. It would have been good. Bye, bruvver.

Cart boy enters with a cart and **Shrimps's** *body is lifted onto it.* **The boys** *gather round as he is wheeled off. They are all very cold. They follow the cart and* **Samuel** *walks behind them. Song.*

Scene Eight

A flat roof above a market stall. **Street boys** *are asleep, wrapped in sacks and huddled together for warmth.* **Jim** *sits slightly apart from the others. He is coughing. Gradually the boys wake up. It is very cold.*

DAVEY Anyone got any food? No-one? Whose turn is it to go to the shops?

BILLY Skipping Jim, must be your turn. And don't let anyone see you coming back, or we'll all get caught.

JIM I'm no good at pinching stuff. I don't like doing it.

BILLY You've got to learn, or go begging.

JIM I'm no good at that, either. I hate it when people just walk past me as if they can't see me.

DAVEY Dance for it, Jim, like you used to do.

JIM I don't feel like dancing any more.

DAVEY Come on, we'll get our own. Don't expect us to help you, that's all.

Davey and the other **boys** *go.*

BILLY Davey means it, you know. You gotta join in and do the same as us, or you'll starve.

JIM I don't want to go on like this any more, Billy. I might as well be where Shrimps is.

BILLY There ain't no other way to be, unless you go back to that workhouse. Or that school. Gotta live somehow. *(**Billy** goes)*

JIM School! What's the point of going there, now Shrimps is dead? Wouldn't mind sitting by the fire though, nice and warm. Just for a day though, just to get out of the cold. *(**Shrimps**'s voice)* What d'you fink, bruvver? Fink? It's too cold to fink. You'll perish to death if you sit here finking. *(own voice)* I don't have to stay there. Just as long as it suits me. That's all right, ain't it? *(**Jim** goes)*

Scene Nine

*The Ragged School. A big fire is burning. Ragged **children** sit on benches* *writing on slates. **Dr Barnardo** paces round looking at their work.*

***Jim** sidles in and goes to sit by the fire.*

BARNARDO You've worked very well today, children. I'm very pleased with you, and I know your parents will be too.

CHILD 1 Teacher, will you tell us the story of the man with the boat?

CHILD 2 Oh, yes, the Noah story, teacher.

BARNARDO Why do you like that story so much?

CHILD 1 Because Noah was kind and wanted to give a home to the animals.

BARNARDO Do you not think he should have given a home to the people?

CHILD 2 No, because animals are nicer than people.

BARNARDO Is that so? Why is that?

CHILD 2 They don't hit you.

CHILD 3 Anyway, people can look after themselves, but animals can't. That's why Mister Noah built the ark for them. The animals couldn't make one for themselves.

*The **children** laugh.*

CHILD 2 But none of the other people made a boat.

CHILD 1 Mister Noah was special.

BARNARDO *(laughs)* I think you are right. He was very special.

CHILD So will you tell us the story?

BARNARDO I don't think I need to. I think you know the story very well. Ah well, all right, tomorrow maybe. But now I think it's time for the hymn and home.

Disappointment from the **children**.

BARNARDO Stand now.

All the **children** *stand except* **Jim**. *Barnardo glances at him and* **Jim** *looks away. Led by* **Barnardo**, *the* **children** *sing a hymn loudly and cheerfully, then with a chorus of 'Goodbye, teacher', they run out of the classroom.* **Barnardo** *straightens up the benches. Then he comes and sits by* **Jim**.

BARNARDO It's time for me to put the lights out. Come on, my boy. It's time to go home now.

JIM Please, mister. Let me stay.

BARNARDO Stay? What for? I'm going to turn the lights out and lock the door. It's quite time for a little boy like you to go home and get to bed. What do you want to stop for?

JIM Please, mister.

BARNARDO You ought to go home at once. Your mother will know the other children have gone. She'll wonder what kept you so late.

JIM I ain't got no mother.

BARNARDO Your father then.

JIM I ain't got no father.

BARNARDO Where are your friends then? Where do you live?

JIM Ain't got no friends. Don't live nowhere.

Barnardo stares at him. He walks away from the fire and back to it again, then sits at his desk, drumming his fingers.

JIM It's the truth, sir, I ain't telling you no lies.

BARNARDO What's your name, child?

JIM Jim. Jim Jarvis.

BARNARDO Tell me, Jim Jarvis, how many boys are there like you? Sleeping out there with no home to go to?

JIM Heaps. More than I can count.

BARNARDO *(after a long, thoughtful pause)* I have thought this for a long time, yet I have never been able to find where the children sleep out at night. Heaps, you say? Shame on us. Shame on us all, Jim Jarvis. What kind of a world is it, where we can allow things like this to happen? Now. If I am willing to give you some hot coffee and a place to sleep in, will you take me to where some of these other boys are?

JIM You wouldn't tell the police?

BARNARDO No. I wouldn't tell the police.

JIM All right. I'll take you.

Scene Ten

Barnardo's study.

JIM *(to Barnardo)* I never seen a grown-up look so sad, and that's the truth. You just looked and looked, as if you couldn't believe your eyes. I was shivering next to you, and I thought you were never going to move or stop looking. I thought you were going to stay there all night.

*Jim and Barnardo come out and stand in front of the audience as if at the roof-top market stall. The **street boys** are lying round them in their rags, coughing and shivering.*

BARNARDO So this is where you live, is it?

JIM Yes, mister.

BARNARDO I'll tell you something, Jim. I will never rest until I have raised enough money to give every one of these boys somewhere to live. I don't know how I'm going to do it.

JIM No, mister. There's an awful lot of 'em.

BARNARDO I need to tell their stories to rich people, and ask them for money to help us. And I'm going to start with yours.

JIM Mine, mister?

BARNARDO Yes, Jim. I'm going to start with you. I'm going to give you a home.

Barnardo goes to sit at his desk.

BARNARDO Now, Jim. Tell me your story.

JIM *(to audience)* That's why he wanted to know my story, see? He told the rich people that there were lots of children like me who couldn't help themselves, and they gave him money to give us a home. Home. And there's nothing to keep us here. Can't believe that, I can't. No bars on the window or locks on the doors. No beatings. I could run away tomorrow if I wanted to. But I don't, see? I'm Jim Jarvis, I am. And this is my home.

Staging the play

Street Child includes many different locations and a wide variety of characters, so when staging the play you will need to make clear where the action is taking place and who the characters are. You might decide to build a set that represents a slum area of London in the 1860s, but if you try to make this look realistic, how will you represent the other locations, for example: the kitchen of the Big House; the wharf; the circus; inside the workhouse?

SET

Start by thinking of the play as a story and the cast of the play working together as a group storyteller. A good storyteller keeps the story flowing, so try to avoid cumbersome scene changes that slow down the action. There should be no gaps between scenes unless you want a pause for special effect. Rather than dividing the acting space into specific locations, use it simply as an open space in which the story is brought alive through action and group work.

These are some possible layouts:

1. an open space with tiered areas at the back (the school stage if you have one) and with audience on three sides

2. an open space on the floor of the hall with audience all round (this type of staging is known as 'in the round')

3. an acting area on the floor of the hall with audience on two sides and with members of the cast at each end (this is called a 'traverse' staging)

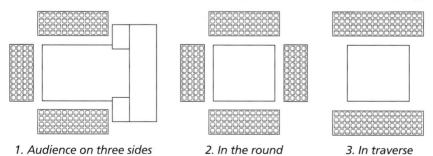

1. Audience on three sides   2. In the round   3. In traverse

With all these layouts, you will need to indicate the location of each scene so that the audience knows how the story moves from place to place. A simple way of doing this would be to use a screen suspended above the acting area in a position that can be clearly seen by all members of the audience, and to project on to the screen the location of each scene: 'Kitchen of the Big House', 'On board *The Lily*', etc. You could also project pictures of the slums, the river, the wealthier part of town, or pictures of Dr Barnardo and his Ragged School.

STYLE

You will want to make some parts of the play as naturalistic as possible, as if you are recreating actual moments from the past. But you can also use stylised acting techniques (where characters do not behave as in real life) to achieve dramatic effects, and to help establish the scene changes.

 Drama

In groups

7

A. Plan a possible beginning for the play, noting your ideas down on a sheet of paper. The opening image should create an impression of London bustling with activity, but it also needs to convey the human desperation underneath: poor people living on the edge, worrying about where their next meal is going to come from. Decide on the types of characters and activities which will appear on stage – they don't all have to come from the script of *Street Child*.

B. Improvise a street scene in your groups, playing some of the characters you have chosen. Then work together with the other groups to create the opening moments of the play. Build up the scene step by step, to create a social picture of London at the time the play is set. Not all the people in the scene will be poor. While this is happening, the next scene could be set up in the middle of the action, and the image of the London street may gradually freeze to reveal Jim and Dr Barnardo.

7–13

C. Now look ahead to the next few scene changes: from Dr Barnardo's study (Act 1, Scene 1) to Mrs Hodder's pie shop (Scene 2), to the Jarvis household (Scene 3), and to the Big House (Scene 4). Try to work out ways of moving from one scene to another avoiding gaps and keeping the story flowing.

A good performance of the play will depend on the actors working well together as an ensemble (team), supporting and listening to each other. Remember that you are telling the story to an audience, so it can be helpful to have one person in each group looking carefully at the images as an 'outside eye', feeding back what is being communicated.

CREATING CHARACTERS

There are many different character types in the play, for example: the old skinflint Mr Spink, the good-hearted Rosie, the fearsome Mr Barrack, the violent Grimy Nick, the treacherous Madame Juglini, and Shrimps, Jim's loyal 'bruvver'. When building a character you will need to think about how the character is expressed through posture, movement and voice.

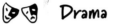 **Drama**

In pairs

A. Find out as much as you can about Mr Spink by reading the scene in which he appears (Act 1, Scene 3). What does the scene suggest about his character and appearance?   10-13

B. What would be his normal facial expression? Experiment with making face shapes that would seem to fit Mr Spink. Do this with a partner as a mirror – your partner making the shapes that you make so that you can see how they look. Choose the one that fits best, but make sure it is a shape you can hold fixed for a long time without relaxing it.

C. Now make the body posture that would go with the face. How would Mr Spink stand? He walks with a stick, so this will affect his normal body shape. Try walking with this body shape, keeping the face shape at the same time.
  ● How would Mr Spink enter the room where Ma lies in her sick bed?
  ● How does the tapping of his stick affect the other characters?

D. Body shapes affect the sound of the voice. Holding the shape you have created, speak one of Mr Spink's lines: 'No money, no rent. No rent, no room. Oh dear.' Speak the line to your partner. Then add other lines.

Staying in character is quite tiring, but while you are performing it be careful not to relax back into yourself. If you do this, the character loses its power immediately. What you have created with the face, posture, walk and voice is a character 'mask'. When the mask is on, you are the character, when you take it off, you are yourself again. Make sure that each time you put on the character 'mask' you sustain it for as long as you are in the scene.

COSTUME

As there are lots of characters in the play it is likely that each person will have to play more than one part, so there could be many costume changes during the performance. These may be done at the side of the acting area. Actors could wear a simple black T-shirt and shorts underneath the costumes so that they only change the top costume. It does not matter if the audience can see the changes taking place.

Most of the characters in the play are poor people, so it will be fairly easy to create their costumes out of old clothes. For the street children, you can make up shirts, blouses, trousers and skirts from cast-off clothes, but one of the tasks will be to make them look genuinely old and dirty. Here are a few tips for treating the costumes to achieve this effect:

- Rip or tear the clothes from the seams (cuts with scissors are too obvious).

- To create an aged or soiled look, sprinkle the garment with Fuller's Earth Powder or wood ash and leave it to hang for 5-10 minutes, then gently shake it to distribute the powder evenly. Do not rub the powder in.

- To create a stained effect, dip (but don't soak) garments in cold tea then hang them out to dry.

- Tear trimmings off and let buttons hang loosely.

Older women wore long skirts, and shawls, mainly in black, grey or dark colours, and with aprons which should be white but show the marks of work and street living. The men's jackets were long and these may have to be made specially. Mr Spink and Mr Barrack would wear jackets, but Grimy Nick and Mr Cockerill might wear just shirts and old trousers. The circus people – the Juglinis, clowns and acrobats – could be dressed in more flamboyant and colourful clothes, rather like circus people today. Turn to page 89 to get an idea of how Dr Barnardo dressed.

By far the biggest speaking part is Jim Jarvis. You could divide up the part so that sections can be played by different actors. Jim could wear a cap and a neckerchief and then hand these on to the person who takes over the character.

SOUND EFFECTS

Victorian London was a crowded, noisy place, and, like today, there were many traffic jams, though of horse-drawn carriages not cars. As a general rule it is better to use live sounds as part of the scene, but there are parts of the play where recorded sound might help to create the right atmosphere, for example: the sounds of horses' hooves and carriages in the street, gates and locks in the workhouse.

⟨?? ??⟩ Discussion

In groups Look through the play for moments when you think live or recorded sounds might be used. Decide how you would create the sounds. Try to think of ways of creating the sound live on stage, before you opt for recorded sounds.

Most of the sound effects you will need can be found on BBC tapes and CDs. Most large local libraries have some sound effects CDs in the music section.

LIGHTING

Keep the lighting as simple as possible. Most scenes can take place under general lighting but you can also use lighting to define stage areas and create atmosphere. For example, the light in the workhouse school room could come from one direction as if through a window high up on the wall. The gloomy atmosphere of other parts of the workhouse could be created with candles (but be sure to enclose them in lanterns so that the flame is not exposed). The circus should be bright and colourful, so you might think of using coloured spotlights. The atmosphere of Dr Barnardo's study could be created by a paraffin table lamp.

Work on and around the script

POVERTY IN THE VICTORIAN ERA

During the Victorian era, the population of England expanded from 16 million in 1840 to 26 million in 1880. As the population increased more and more people moved to the cities to work in the mills and factories of the Industrial Revolution. Industry created wealth and the Victorians built many new impressive buildings. The slums also expanded. These were grim places where there was no proper water supply, and the streets were filthy with sewage. Many infants died from illness and disease; in the poorest areas, one in two children died before the age of one. Despite the high death rate the child population increased rapidly.

A London slum

Dr Barnardo visited the slums many times. In the passage below, he
describes what he saw on one such visit.

In a room … were nine persons – father and mother, aged about
40, a youth of 19, a girl of 17, three younger boys and two girls.
There also lived with them a cousin and a lodger. A single flock
bed on the floor occupied one end of the room. At the hour I called
all were in that bed except the lodger and the mother, who was
washing at a tub … It appeared that all of them were out of work
and had been so for some time. The poor woman came down to
the street door to talk to me – 'The worst of it is, I can't hope to
keep the girls decent, living as we do.'

Barnardo's notes on children taken into his care give further glimpses
of life in the London slums.

E.S.F (12) and W.F. (7) In a wretched back room, void of
furniture, these girls (the younger one is a lifelong cripple from
hip-joint disease) were living with their father. No bed. Children
have slept on a few old rags on the floor, the father in a chair lent
to him by his landlady. Mother dead. Father honest and
industrious, but has been driven to the wall through sheer inability
to gain employment.

Children who were able to find work sold flowers, matches, cakes,
swept the streets or looked after horses. Older girls looked after younger
brothers and sisters.

🎭 Still pictures

In groups

A. Choose one child from the photograph below. Make up a name and invent a life story for that child.

B. Create two still pictures capturing moments in the life of the child you have chosen. Still pictures can tell stories, by making us think about what happened before the picture and what might happen after it. Try to construct pictures that tell a story. Share the pictures with the class. After each picture, spend a few moments discussing what you saw, the characters, the place, what is happening. What does the picture tell us about life in the slums?

C. Take each picture and extend it into a short scene of no more than 15 seconds, including words and action. As each scene is brief, make sure that it communicates exactly what you want it to say, the 'essence' of the moment. Start and end each scene with a freeze.

These children are from a slum area in London at around the time Dr Barnardo was setting up his homes for destitute children. They are queuing for a farthing breakfast (one quarter of a penny) from the Salvation Army.

Report

On your own Research and write a report on the lives of poor children in the Victorian slums (there is a list of some of the books you might use in the Resources on page 112).

H

The watercress girl

These are the actual words of a girl who spent her days selling watercress on the streets of London for a few pence to give to her mother. The girl calls the watercress 'creases'.

'I go about the streets with water-creases, crying, "Four bunches a penny, water-creases." I am just eight years old, that's all, and I've a big sister, and a brother and a sister younger than I am. I used to go to school but I wasn't there long. My mother took me away because the master whacked me.

'The creases is bad now, that I haven't been out with 'em for three days. They're so cold, people won't buy 'em; for when I goes up to them, they say. "They'll freeze our bellies." I get the creases from the market with another girl, as must be about fourteen, 'cos she does her back hair up. When we've bought a lot, we sits down on a doorstep, and ties up the bunches. We never go home till we've sold out, but if it's very late, then I buys a penn'orth of pudden, which is very nice with gravy.

'When the snow is on the ground, there's creases. I bears the cold – you must; so I puts my hand under my shawl, though it hurts them to take hold of the creases, especially when we takes 'em to the pump to wash 'em. No; I never see children crying – it's no use.

'Sometimes I make a great deal of money. One day I took 1s. 6d., and the creases cost 6d., but it isn't often I get such luck as that. I oftener makes 3d. or 4d. than 1s., and then I'm at work, crying "Creases, four bunches a penny, creases!" from six in the morning to about ten. I always give my mother my money, she's so very good to me. She doesn't often beat me, but, when she do, she don't play with me. She's very poor and goes out cleaning rooms sometimes. I ain't got no father, he's a father-in-law. He grinds scissors, and he's very good to me. I don't mean by that that he says kind things to me, for he hardly ever speaks. When

I gets home, after selling creases, I stops at home. I puts the room to rights; mother don't make me do it, I does it myself. I cleans the chairs, though there's only two to clean. I takes a scrubbing brush and flannel, and scrubs the floor – that's what I do three or four times a week.'

✐ Charity Report 🎭

In groups Imagine that you have been asked to write a report for a charity on families who depend on money they earn in the street. Take as your subject the watercress girl. Before writing your report, try to find out more about the girl by 'hot-seating' her, that is, by one person taking on her role and answering questions from the rest of the group. Do the same with her mother, her stepfather, and her friend in the street.

In the report you will need to present a clear picture of how poverty affects the lives of these people, and you will also need to make some specific suggestions about how to change things for the better.

Jim Jarvis's family

In the play, Jim Jarvis never knew his father. Because of poor living conditions and low standards of health, people died at a much younger age than they do today, and many children lost one or both parents. After Jim's father's death, Ma would have had to earn money to bring up her family. Many single mothers were the only breadwinners. Remember that there was no social security like today, so if you couldn't earn money you had to rely on charity or face being sent to the workhouse. You also had to pay for the doctor and any medicines needed. Here is how one single mother described her life:

I myself had some very hard times, as I had to go out to work in the mill and put the baby out to nurse. I had to get up by four in the morning, and get my baby out of bed, wash and dress it, and then leave home by five, as I had half an hour's walk to take my baby to my mother's, and then go to my work and stand all day till half past five at night and then walk home again with my baby. I had to do this with three of them.

Margaret Llewelyn Davies

☺☹ Role Play

In pairs

A. Go back to a time before the play started but after the death of Jim's father. Imagine that Ma has been working for two years for her family but now her health is failing and she knows she can't carry on. If she stops work, the children will go hungry, and if this happens she may have to consider giving them up for adoption. Many of the women who adopted babies were themselves poor. Their houses were called 'baby farms' and sometimes the money ran out and the babies starved.

Situation   Ma talks to a friend (who also has a large family and just one room) about what she should do.

B. Ma now lives in the room in the tenement with her three children but has fallen behind with the rent.

Situation   A well-meaning neighbour sees her distress and pays a visit to the landlord, Mr Spink, and tries to persuade him to let Ma and her children stay in the room.

Street children

In the middle of the nineteenth century there were about 100,000 destitute children in London alone. These were children who, as one observer at the time said, 'have known no guidance from parents, master or relative, but have been flung into the streets through neglect, through viciousness, or as outcasts from utter destitution … have been either untaught, mistaught, maltreated, neglected, regularly trained to vice, or fairly turned into the streets to shift for themselves'. Gangs of marauding children inhabited the streets and alleyways, stealing to survive, and children as young as six were often brought before the court. The theft of a loaf could lead to six months in prison, and to sleep in the streets was a crime under the Vagrancy Act and could lead to imprisonment. But to many children imprisonment seemed no worse and possibly better than the misery of living on the streets.

The passage on page 84 is an account by a 15 year old boy, Jack, who became a pickpocket after running away from home to escape his father who beat him. He fell in with a very experienced pickpocket who taught him to pick people's money 'so as they won't feel it'. He describes a day's work at a public hanging.

I did 4s. 6d. at the hanging – two handkerchiefs, and a purse with 2s. in it – the best purse I ever had; but I've only done three or four purses. The reason is because I've never been well-dressed. If I went near a lady, she would say, 'Tush, tush, you ragged fellow!' and would shrink away. But I would rather rob from the rich than the poor; they miss it less. At the fire in Monument-yard I did 5s. 7d. – 3s. in silver and 2s. 3d. in handkerchiefs, and 4d. for the three pairs of gloves. I sell my handkerchiefs in Petticoat Lane. I have been in prison three times in Brixton, three times in the Old Horse (Bridewell), once in the Steel and once in Maidstone. Every time I came out harder than I went in. I've had four floggings; it was bad enough, a flogging was, while it lasted; but when I got out I soon forgot about it. If I had been better treated I should have been a better lad. If one's in prison for begging, one's laughed at. The others say, 'Begging! Oh, you cadger!' So a boy is partly forced to steal for his character. If boys run away, and has to shelter in low lodging houses – and many runs away from cruel treatment at home – they meet there with boys such as me, or as bad, and the devil soon lays his hand on them. If an innocent boy gets into a lodging house, he'll not be innocent long.

Street children

 Writing

On your own

A. Imagine that Jack has been arrested once again for stealing and that this time he will have to serve a longer sentence and suffer more flogging. If you were his lawyer, how might you present his case in court? Are there arguments you could use which may support a case for a lighter sentence? Write down the key points of your argument.

B. Before he met Dr Barnardo, Jim Jarvis was once sent to prison for sleeping outdoors. This incident is not mentioned in the play. Write an account of Jim's life in prison, as if he was speaking, in his imagination, to his mother's ghost. Decide if, like Jack the pickpocket, he was made harder by the experience of prison. What does he feel about being locked away?

Life in the workhouse

In Act 1, Scene 6, Ma and Jim are taken to the workhouse. For the Victorians, to be sent to the workhouse was about the worst fate that you could suffer. Anybody who was too old or sick to work and had no support from family or charities was sent there. Life in the workhouse was intended to be less attractive than any means of earning a living outside. Workhouses were rather like prisons in that the inmates were locked in and had no chance of leaving without permission from the authorities. The regime was strict and the discipline harsh, making the poor people feel they were being punished for their poverty. Many destitute people preferred to beg and keep their freedom than to submit to the harsh conditions.

Once admitted to the workhouse, men and women were separated to prevent childbearing, and the children were sent to the workhouse school. The quality of education was poor, but it offered instruction in basic skills to help the children find employment. The job of the schoolmaster or schoolmistress was to instruct the boys and girls 'for three of the waking hours at least every day in reading, writing and the principles of the Christian religion, and give them other instruction in the habits of usefulness, industry and virtue'. But it was difficult to get good teachers. In a workhouse in Salisbury, for example, it was reported that the schoolmistress could not write and the schoolmaster was himself a pauper who had been admitted to the workhouse for excessive drinking.

⊂꜀꜂⊃ Discussion

In groups Read Act 1, Scene 7, and discuss Mr Barrack's teaching methods.

- How different is his teaching from what you have experienced?

- What is wrong with Mr Barrack as a teacher?

Victorian Education

Attitudes about what is right and what is wrong change over time. The extracts below are taken from a book called *Parental Care for the Salvation of Children*, published by The Religious Tract Society, a Christian organisation, in 1839.

Children are sinners

A parent, who desires his children to become wise unto salvation, should especially endeavour to fix deeply on their hearts the conviction that they are undone sinners … Children that 'come not to Christ' will be plunged into the 'abyss' where at the bottom 'roll the fiery waves of hell'. There the child's soul, departed from its body, sinks into the burning lake. Oh, what are its shrieks, its wailings, and its horror! The waves of the lake, that burns with fire and brimstone, close over the miserable victim of sin; it sinks and sinks for ever!

Corporal punishment

Almost in infancy, children manifest a disobedient disposition; a determination if possible, to have their will gratified. The first efforts of this disposition should be repressed by unyielding firmness … 'Thou shalt beat him with the rod, and shalt deliver his soul from hell.' … a parent should not correct in passion … very different is the effect if punishment is inflicted with calmness; with cool representation to the child, that his parent punishes him with sorrow, from a sense of duty, because he has committed a great sin, and has greatly offended God.

Discussion and Presentation

In groups

A. Corporal punishment is now banned in British schools. What are your attitudes to corporal punishment?

B. Imagine that a group of Victorian reformers consult you on how to improve teaching for pauper children. Bear in mind that the reformers are genuinely trying to help the children, and they want practical ideas that can be implemented. Make notes on your conclusions and share them with the rest of the class.

Death of Shrimps

The character of Shrimps is based on a real-life street child called John Somers, known to his street friends as 'Carrots' because of his red hair. Carrots lived rough on the streets from the age of seven. He never knew his father, and his mother turned him out of the house. On the streets he sold cigar lights, delivered papers, and polished shoes. Whenever he had earned a few coins for food, his mother returned to rob him and spend the money in a gin shop. If he had no money she would beat and kick him.

In the play Shrimps becomes a 'bruvver' to Jim. Though he is destitute, he has a lot of spirit and a good sense of humour. He even jokes when he is ill. He refuses to go to hospital for fear of being returned to the workhouse.

 **Drama**

In groups

A. Devise and perform your own version of the scene in which Shrimps's body is placed on the cart by the street children. Then devise and insert 'flash-backs' of short episodes of Shrimps's life into the scene, for example: his first meeting with Jim, his bootlace trick on people in the queue, his clownish dance. You could also invent some episodes that do not appear in the play, for example: a moment when he sees his mother coming for his money and he and Jim try to hide.

B. Link the sections with the verses on page 88 from the Victorian song 'The Burial of the Linnet'.

cont...

Found in the garden, – dead in his beauty.
Ah! that a linnet should die in the Spring!
Bury him, comrades, in pitiful duty,
Muffle the dinner bell, solemnly ring.

Bury him softly – white wool around him,
Kiss his poor feathers – the first kiss and last;
Tell his poor widow kind friends have found him:
Plant his poor grave with whatever grows fast.

Farewell, sweet singer! dead in thy beauty,
Silent through summer, though other birds sing,
Bury him, comrades, in pitiful duty,
Muffle the dinner bell, mournfully ring.

*A linnet is a small songbird, a finch

To find out what happened to the real 'Carrots' on which the character of Shrimps is based, turn to pages 92–3.

Victorian Reformers

As child destitution increased so did the will to do something about it. The church, in particular, took an active role in attempts to improve the lives of these children. As part of an effort to remove the bands of children from the streets, a campaign for compulsory education was begun. Ragged Schools were set up in the 1840s by Lord Shaftesbury, with the aim of teaching Christian morality to children who might otherwise turn to crime. The schools taught reading, writing and calculation and provided religious instruction. Teachers were hard-working and the pupils learned how to read and acquired new skills, enabling them to get jobs in useful trades and occupations. It was in a Ragged School in an old donkey-shed in Hope Place, Stepney, that Jim Jarvis met Dr Barnardo.

Dr Thomas John Barnardo, 1845–1905

Thomas John Barnardo was born in Dublin, Ireland. In 1862, Thomas was influenced by an Evangelical Revival which took place in Dublin. The Evangelicals believed that through the Bible the poor could find new faith and courage to improve their lives and reduce poverty. Thomas was converted to Christianity, and from this point religion guided his entire life. He believed he had been called by God to help make people's lives better through social reform. He organised Bible classes for people in the Dublin slums, and within a short time set up classes for people from all walks of life. Though he was pleased with this work, he was restless. In 1866 he volunteered to become a missionary in China and he left Dublin for London to prepare himself for his new job. He moved to Coburn Street, Stepney, in the East End, one of the poorest areas of London, where he discovered that the living conditions were far worse than they were in Dublin.

Dr Barnardo

In 1866 Barnardo registered as a medical student at the London Hospital in Whitechapel intending to lead a medical mission to China. During an outbreak of cholera, he called at many houses in Stepney to tend the sick and dying. He wrote afterwards that all around him 'were men and women, boys and girls, steeped in ignorance and sin, veritable heathens whose souls needed the illumination of the Gospel'.

Barnardo wanted to do something to help children living in poverty. His first step was to teach in a Ragged School. Children flocked to the school in such numbers that he decided to open a larger school of his own. He rented an old shed which had been used as a donkey stable and, with the help of some fellow medical students, cleaned it up and added seats and books. Barnardo described the first days of the new school:

...into this old, disused, donkey-shed ... we gathered a crowd of idle, ill-washed children, on two nights a week and on Sundays, arranging the week nights so that two of us should be on duty at a time, while on Sundays we were all there. ... There it was that I had my first indication of an inspiration towards what proved to be my life's work.

69–71 The inspiration came in the form of Jim Jarvis. In Act 3, Scene 9 of the play, we see the meeting between Jim and Dr Barnardo. The dialogue is almost exactly as Dr Barnardo recorded it from their real-life meeting. A little later, after some food and drink, Jim took Barnardo through dirty alleyways to an old clothes shop in Petticoat Lane.

There on the open roof, lay a confused group of boys, all asleep. I counted eleven ... The rags that most of them wore were mere apologies for clothes ... I realised the terrible fact that they were absolutely homeless and destitute, and were almost certainly but examples of many others: it seemed as though the hand of God Himself had suddenly pulled aside the curtain which concealed from my view the untold miseries of forlorn child-life upon the streets of London.

Home For Boys

In 1867, with the help of charitable donations, Barnardo rented a large house in Stepney and converted it into dormitories. He started with 25 boys, who were washed and given new clothes. The first Dr Barnardo Home for destitute children was founded.

The donkey-shed where Dr Barnardo established his Ragged School, and some of the children he taught there

The Boys Home in Stepney Causeway

With only limited funds, Dr Barnardo was worried about letting the home go into debt. One day a homeless boy called John Somers, nicknamed 'Carrots', arrived at the home, hoping for a bed. All the money collected so far had already been spent, however. Dr Barnardo faced a difficult decision: whether to take Carrots and risk going into debt or to send him away.

---

೫೩ ୧୨ Discussion

In groups Put yourself in Barnardo's position. What will you do with Carrots? Discuss this carefully before making a decision. If you agree to take Carrots, you are risking going into debt, and you will need to think about what you will say to the next child who comes to the home asking to be admitted.

In the event, Dr Barnardo turned Carrots away, promising him the next available bed. A few days later, Carrots was found dead near London Bridge. He had died from exhaustion and exposure. Barnardo was stunned by Carrots's death, feeling he was to blame, and he vowed never again to turn away a child in need. He ordered this sign to be placed outside the Stepney home:

NO DESTITUTE CHILD EVER REFUSED ADMISSION

 **Drama**

In groups Devise a scene that pieces together the last few hours of Carrots's life from the time when he left the Stepney home to his body being found. This was a crowded part of London so many people would have seen him. Choose six witnesses who each can offer a different part of the story. They may not all be poor people, and each character will reveal something of themselves in their witness account. Perform the witness 'statements' in sequence to create a verbal picture of Carrots's last hours.

Life in the Stepney Home for Boys

A child on being admitted to the home would follow a routine. He would first be photographed, then bathed, washed, and given a haircut. He would collect a uniform and be given a bed and locker in one of the dormitories. From then on he would follow the daily timetable.

5.25am	Bugle: Boys dress, pray, fling windows wide open.
5.45am	Make beds, polish floors, clean windows and brasses.
6.00am	Wash.
6.30am	Drill in the playground.
7.00am	Breakfast and family prayer with Bible reading and hymn singing.
7.40am	Clear tables and sweep and dust room.
8.00am	Band practice.
8.30am	Inspection parade and fall in for school.
10.00am	Ten-minute interval between lessons.
11.30am	Break.
12.00pm	Dinner.
12.30pm	Clear dining hall, wash, brush up, play.
1.30pm	Inspection and drill parade.
1.40pm	School and workshops.

4.45pm	School ends. Wash and play.
5.45pm	Clear workshops.
6.00pm	Tea, family prayers and service.
6.40pm	Play followed by baths.
7.00pm	Night school for older boys.
8.30pm	All to dormitories.
9.00pm	Lights out and silence.

In the workshops the boys were taught skills as a form of self-discipline and to help them become employable as tailors, shoemakers, carpenters, brushmakers, engineers and bakers. All the household work was done by the boys themselves: they were their own cooks, waiters, cleaners and they made their own beds.

☺☺ Discussion

In groups Read the timetable. Why was it constructed in this way? What do you think were its advantages and disadvantages?

Home For Girls

In 1873, Barnardo's first home for girls was opened. His hope was 'to train up a band of kitchen maids, housemaids, parlour-maids, laundry-maids, dairymaids and cooks to meet the great demand existing everywhere for instructed female servants.' It was based on the idea of a village, with a school, infirmary and laundry and open areas with flowerbeds. The Village was an instant success. A reporter who visited the Village commented:

Each cottage is presided over by a woman … capable of both firmness and gentleness, of an affectionate disposition, and accustomed to manage children. She is called Mother by the little ones under her care; her will is law … The rooms in which the girls sleep are plain and homelike. Small iron bedsteads painted green, and covered with a counterpane bearing the name of the home woven in the centre, occupy the corners … The older girls take it in turn to help cook the dinner, to lay the cloth, to keep the house in order, and to imitate Mother in everything she does. Every girl is taught to love truth, to be gentle and modest … to regard each other as adopted sisters.

✍ Writing

On your own When Sarah, 12, was admitted to the Village Home, Barnardo made these notes about her:

> This little girl, after wandering about the streets, forlorn, for several days, in the dead of winter, sheltering where she could, found her way to the Refuge door, sobbing bitterly, and was at once admitted. Her mother was in hospital from a painful disease, which has since caused her death. Father died several years ago … the girl was becoming demoralised. Was learning to steal.

Sarah learns to read and write in the home, and starts a diary which becomes a record of her thoughts about her new life and the life she has left. Write some of her thoughts as they appear in the diary. This may be extracts written over a period of time.

What was life like for Barnardo children? Many said that Barnardo's gave them the security of belonging to a family, some remember the opportunities to learn and develop skills, others felt lonely or were bullied; a few, sad to say, suffered physical abuse.

The comments below are by adults today who, as children, lived in a Barnardo's home.

> To look at, the grounds were lovely, the lawns, the flowerbeds and the almond trees. But there was a high fence and wrought-iron gates, and once they clanged behind you, you were shut in and you didn't feel free.
>
> Agnes Bowley

> Until I came to Barnardo's I'd been shunted from relation to relation, and I finally ended up in the arms of the law. They encouraged me to join a band, and for the first time in my life I felt a real sense of comradeship. I played the silver bugle with pride and realised that I had finally begun to enjoy life.
>
> Malcolm Lang

You had no personal life. Everyone was known by numbers. Mine was number nine and everything I had had to be chainstitched with the number nine. What I remember above all was the harshness of the staff. We all had to have pudding basin haircuts and they regularly combed through our hair for nits.

Mary

I came under Barnardo's care when I was eight years old. I had never attended school nor had I mixed with other boys. Men were ogres to me. I was disturbed, distressed and wayward. Under Barnardo's influence all that changed. They taught by quiet example and commitment the merits of self-reliance, integrity of purpose and pride in competency, however lowly the task.

Bill Hill

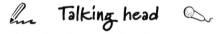

Talking head

H

On your own Look at the photographs of Barnardo children below and on page 97. Choose one of the children and imagine that the child is thirty years older now. Since leaving Dr Barnardo's your chosen character has got on well in life. Work out what their life circumstances might be now. Choose one moment which the character remembers especially well of their life in the home. Why is this particular memory important? Using all the information about life in the homes, devise a 'talking head' for your character. The character is talking as if to a television camera about their memory of a childhood event.

Barnardo children

From novel to playscript

The playscript of *Street Child* is an adaptation by Berlie Doherty of her novel of the same name, and the scenes follow the sequence of events in the original story. Not every part of the novel has been included in the play; this is because, in a play, stage action takes the place of description and the inner thoughts of the characters. A few incidents have been changed to keep the drama flowing. Compare, for example, Act 3, Scene 3 with the same part of the story in the book. These are the first few paragraphs:

Far away behind him Jim could hear the beating of the drums and the blare of the trumpets and trombones, the roar of the crowd. When he paused to look round he could see the glow of the huge tent and the dark shapes of the caravans parked round the edges of the field. He could just make out which one was Juglini's.

He turned away again and ran until he could run no more. He reached a barn near a farmhouse. The door was open. He crept in and curled himself up in a pile of straw. His last thoughts, as sleep overtook him, were of something that Shrimps had said, long ago.

'I'd rather sleep in a barnful of rats, and I've done that a time or two.'

Jim listened to the scurryings round him. 'Well,' he thought, 'rats is charming company, bruvver. At least they knows where it's warm and dry.'

The cry of the farmyard cockerel woke him up, and the sun striping through the barn roof. Jim lay still and tense, listening to the sound of the farmworkers making their way to the fields. When their voices had died away he went out of the barn. Hens cluttered round him and squawked away again. An old woman, swaying as she walked, came out of the farm building carrying two large pails. She swayed past the barn where Jim crouched, afraid, her skirts sweeping up the hens' grain as they bobbed around her. She went into the milking shed. Jim could hear her talking to the cows, and the low muttering the beasts made.

He dared himself to creep out of the barn again. The old woman had left open the kitchen door. Jim peered in. He could see bread on the table, left over from the men's breakfast – pies and cheeses, a big jug of milk. He slipped in to the kitchen. Maybe if he asked the woman she would give him food. Maybe she would shut him in a back room and go and fetch Grimy Nick. He didn't feel he could ever trust anyone again. He glanced round the yard and sneaked into the kitchen, stuffing as much food as he could in his mouth, cramming his pockets till they bulged. He heard a creak on the stair, swigged from the jug and grabbed one last desperate handful of cheese, and turned to see a girl on the middle step, her hand to her mouth. He dropped the jug and ran. The girl followed him, shouting, the jug clattering still on the flagged floor. The old woman hurried out of her milking shed, and all the farm dogs barked. Jim was away like a hare before a hound, streaking up to the lane.

From Chapter 22, 'On the Run Again'

 Discussion

In pairs What are the differences between the scene in the play and in the novel. What has been left out or added in the writing of the playscript? What might be the reasons for the differences?

🎙 Radio play 🎤

(H)

On your own

A. This is Jim's first ever visit to the country, so many of the things he sees and hears must seem strange to him. Make a list of everything he would notice as being different from his experience as a city boy.

B. Write a section for a radio version of the play, beginning where Jim wakes up in the barn. Include Jim speaking his inner thoughts and feelings about what he sees.

In *Oliver Twist* by Charles Dickens, Oliver is an orphan boy about the same age as Jim Jarvis. Oliver is placed in a workhouse by the parish board 'to be educated, and taught a useful trade'. In the workhouse the food consists of three meals a day of thin gruel (made from oatmeal and water) 'with an onion twice a week and a roll on Sundays'. The boys, forever hungry, draw lots to decide who should ask for more gruel at the next mealtime. It falls to Oliver.

The evening arrived; the boys took their places. The master, in his cook's uniform, stationed himself at the copper; his pauper assistants ranged themselves behind him; the gruel was served out; and a long grace was said over the short commons. The gruel disappeared; the boys whispered to each other, and winked at Oliver; while his next neighbours nudged him. Child as he was, he was desperate with hunger, and reckless with misery. He rose from the table; and advancing to his master, basin and spoon in hand, said, somewhat alarmed at his own temerity:

'Please, sir, I want some more.'

The master was a fat, healthy man; but he turned very pale. He gazed in stupefied astonishment on the small rebel for some seconds, and then clung for support to the copper. The assistants were paralysed with wonder; the boys with fear.

'What!' said the master at length, in a faint voice.

'Please, sir,' replied Oliver, 'I want some more.'

The master aimed a blow at Oliver's head with the ladle; pinioned him in his arms; and shrieked aloud for the beadle.

The board were sitting in solemn conclave, when Mr Bumble rushed into the room in great excitement, and addressing the gentleman in the high chair, said, 'Mr. Limbkins, I beg your pardon, sir! Oliver Twist has asked for more!'

There was a general start. Horror was depicted on every countenance.

'For *more!*' said Mr. Limbkins. 'Compose yourself, Bumble, and answer me distinctly. Do I understand that he asked for more, after he had eaten the supper allotted by the dietary?'

'He did, sir,' replied Bumble.

'That boy will be hung,' said the gentleman in the white waistcoat. 'I know that boy will be hung.'

Nobody controverted the prophetic gentleman's opinion. An

animated discussion took place. Oliver was ordered into instant confinement; and a bill was next morning pasted on the outside of the gate, offering a reward of five pounds to anybody who would take Oliver Twist off the hands of the parish. In other words, five pounds and Oliver Twist were offered to any man or woman who wanted an apprentice to any trade, business or calling.

'I never was more convinced of anything in my life,' said the gentleman in the white waistcoat, as he knocked at the gate and read the bill next morning: 'I never was more convinced of anything in my life, than I am that that boy will come to be hung.'

⊂⊃ ⊂⊃ Discussion

As a class

A. Why is the reaction by the workhouse authorities to Oliver's request so severe?

B. Later in the book, Oliver comes into money through his father's will. If this happened soon after the incident when he asks for more gruel, would it have changed the way the authorities treated Oliver. If so, why?

TV adaptation

On your own

H

Many of Dickens's novels have been adapted for television. Had Dickens been writing today, he might himself have written for television: he is a very good storyteller creating human characters of all types, and he structures the story in episodes so that you want to 'see what happens next week'. Take the scene of Oliver in the workhouse and adapt it for television. The scene will be made up of a number of camera shots, some showing the whole scene from different points of view, others, faces in close-up. Plan each image in sequence, thinking carefully about how the dramatic effect will be built up shot by shot. Include directions in your script, indicating your choice of camera positions.

To find out about how Oliver learns to survive in the streets of Victorian London, join the novel at Chapter 8.

Themes in and around the play

SOCIAL PROBLEMS TODAY

Social Security

Life in our cities today is very different from Victorian times. The worst slums have been demolished, and new building developments have revitalised run-down areas. Far fewer people live in the overcrowded conditions that were common in the past, and the welfare state ensures that families, however desperate their circumstances, are not thrown out on the streets, as Ma and Jim were. The list below includes some of the benefits that people in need can now claim.

- Housing benefit
- Child benefit
- Income support
- Jobseeker's allowance
- Single parent allowance
- Disability allowance
- Council tax benefit
- Family credit

 **Research**

H

On your own Visit a local social security office, to find out about these benefits. Who can claim them? How? Write a short summary, explaining about the benefits for people who might wish to claim them.

As a class If Ma and Jim had been able to claim benefits, how would their lives have been different? Do you think there are any problems with a system that allows people to claim benefits, and how might it be improved?

The money spent on social security is by far the largest part of the government's annual spending. Even so, many families struggle on low incomes, thousands of people are unemployed, and one child in four lives below the official poverty line, so it would be a mistake to assume that all the social problems of Victorian England have been solved.

Housing

The House Condition Survey in 1996 stated that there are 1.5 million homes officially classified as 'unfit for human habitation' in Britain today. Many have unsafe electrical wiring or leaking gas pipes. Some have broken windows and doors and leaking roofs. They may be damp and impossible to heat, making living in them dangerous. Yet nine out of ten of these homes are inhabited, mainly by poor people who do not have the money to improve them. The housing charity Shelter estimates that, in 1998, 400,000 people in England were officially homeless, with almost 49,000 families and individuals placed by local authorities in hostels or bed and breakfast hotels. More than 78,000 families who could not pay their rent or mortgage faced the prospect of their homes being taken away from them. Shelter says that the law is failing because not everyone is able to get housing even when they are homeless, and homeless people often end up in the worst accommodation.

In groups

A. Shelter has pointed out that homeless people are not given help until they reach crisis point. Are there ways of solving the problems of homelessness before this happens? Do homeless people have a right to a home? Should homeless people be involved in decisions about where they live?

B. In Victorian times, destitute families felt they were punished for being poor. Does this happen today? If so, how can it be avoided?

cont...

C. Should we build more homes for poor people, or improve old buildings? Either plan will need money, and to meet the cost the government may have to increase taxation, but most people do not want to pay more taxes. What do you think is the best way of improving the quality of housing for poor families?

Sleeping rough

Many people still sleep rough in our cities. It is estimated that over a year 2,400 people spend some time sleeping rough in London, the total on any given night averaging about 400. Of these very few are under the age of 18 and around 90% are male. Many leave home because of conflicts about their behaviour or with a parent's new partner, or because they have been abused. Around half of rough sleepers have been in prison at some time and 30-50% suffer from mental health problems. As many as half of rough sleepers have a serious alcohol problem. Drug problems are more common among younger rough sleepers.

Sleeping rough on the streets of London

Single people will get assistance under the law only if they are unintentionally homeless (for, example, if they have been thrown out of home). For those who choose to leave home, for whatever reason, life is not easy. In London, there is little hope of a single person being given housing unless they are disabled or have a medical condition.

☺☺ Debate

Living in society places many expectations upon us. Many of us take these expectations for granted: that we will live in a family, go to school, get an education, learn skills, work for a living. Many people who sleep rough have dropped out of this 'system'. Being outside the system means you are free of many of the rules and expectations of society, but getting back in may not be so easy. The longer you stay outside the system, the more difficult may be the way back.

As a class Set up a debate with the motion: 'This house believes that sleeping rough should be against the law.' Divide the class into two groups, and organise speakers supporting and opposing the motion. One group might argue that people should have the freedom to live their lives in the way they wish without interference from others. The other group might say that we have a responsibility to help such people find their way back into society. Try to find arguments to support whichever side of the debate you are on. It does not matter who 'wins' the debate.

Children in care: fostering

Childcare policy has changed in recent years. Much more emphasis is now placed on the importance of the family and of keeping parents and children together. If parents are unable to provide proper care for their children through ill health, homelessness, or if a child is at risk through abuse, the local authority, through its social services department, has the responsibility of providing care for the children. Organisations such as Barnardo's help the social services to provide foster carers and adoptive parents. Fostering provides children with a secure home in a caring environment and allows them to retain links with their birth family. While in care, children remain the responsibility of the social services and are supported by a social worker.

Children stay in care for an average of six months and the aim is to get them back home as soon as possible. Some problems are temporary, with the child returning home after just a few weeks; more persistent problems require planning for the long term. When the child reaches the age of 16, the local authority's responsibility for providing care ceases. Efforts are made to support the child into independent living following a period in care, but the parents must take over the main responsibility for his/her welfare. If parents do not provide proper support then the young person can claim benefit. There are hostels around the country offering shelter to the young homeless. These days the social services make much more effort to keep children in touch with their parents than they did in the past.

☺☺☺ Case studies

In groups

A. Read the following case study.

The case begins a year ago. Stephen, 14, lived with his mother and her new partner following a break-up of the family 5 years ago. The mother has two children with the new partner, then aged 3 and 4, both of them demanding a lot of her attention. Stephen did not get on with his stepfather and they had frequent rows. Stephen's behaviour at school became more and more disruptive and the teachers spoke with the mother and stepfather in an effort to sort out the problem. This led to more rows at home and the stepfather started hitting the boy. The relationship between Stephen and his stepfather deteriorated, and the mother tended to take the stepfather's side. After a time Stephen started to feel afraid to go home. He ran away and was found by the police on the streets of London. His mother then said he could come home only if he promised not to upset his stepfather. Stephen accepted this, but there was an immediate row when he returned, and he ran away again. He was picked up again and the local authority placed him in a foster home. A week ago, he ran away from the home and has not yet returned. Stephen is now 15.

Imagine that you are a group of social workers who have to make a decision about care provision for the family. What is the best way of helping them? Consider as many options as possible before making your decision.

cont...

B. Read the case study below.

A father looks after his four children on his own: two girls aged 12 and 14 and two boys, aged 6 and 8, his wife having died 3 years ago. He works long hours in a factory and is regularly on the early shift starting at 6.00am. Though he does his best, he is not well organised with the shopping and cleaning. Mealtimes are erratic, and the children have got into the habit of buying meals from fast-food shops. The boys' school is concerned that they are coming to school looking dirty and a member of staff has made a home visit. The father admits that he is finding it difficult to manage, but he can't afford to lose his job. He loves his children and wants life to be better for them. No relations or grandparents live close by. He reluctantly seeks help from the social services and agrees to accept their proposal that the children be taken into care for a time to help him get on his feet. Two girls go into one foster home, the two boys into another. The boys are well looked after by a caring couple, and they settle in quite happily. The girls are also placed in a good foster home, but they are worried about their dad and keep turning up at home. Dad tries to take them back to their foster parents but they keep returning and dad contacts social services unsure what he should do next.

If you were the two girls what would you want to happen next? What could you suggest to the social services?

Street children in other countries

We may like to think that the problem of destitute children living in city streets has now disappeared. The truth, however, is that it still exists in many cities of the world, as can be seen from the following accounts by journalists and observers.

Bucharest, Romania

It is a terrifying experience to follow Dan into the hole he considers home. The door is a manhole cover on the edge of a park near Bucharest's Gara de Nord subway station. He squeezes through and descends on iron rungs into a dark, stifling and dirty space. Huge, warm pipes along one wall make hissing noises. Rats scuttle past his feet. The stench of urine and excrement is overwhelming. 'Here it is,' he shrugs. It is difficult to read any emotion on his young face. Dan and three other ragged boys, all in their mid-teens, have spread torn cardboard boxes on the floor. They are grateful to have this warm place for the coming winter. In other parts of the Romanian capital, homeless children have even managed to rig up electricity for makeshift lights.

One of the kings of the Gara de Nord, 'Michael the Blonde', thinks he is about 19 years old but he is not sure. He and his cohorts control entry to the warmer entrances of the tunnels, sometimes extorting payment. The younger children appear desperate for human contact – even with strangers. Nine year-old Ciprian, for example, holds a foreign visitor's hand tightly and calls her 'Mama'.

from *Children of the Tunnels* by Louise Branson

In Guatemala City, street children live by selling bananas, scavenging through garbage and sleeping in doorways and on pavements. Here the children face an even worse threat than hunger, the threat of being murdered by the police, security guards who go around the city practising what is referred to in Guatemala as 'social cleansing'. The other danger is death from addiction to solvents. On June 2, 1997, Edvin Leonel Sanai Sirin, a street child aged 15, died. This is how his death was reported by an observer.

Guatemala City, Central America

Last week I was out on the streets late at night with the Casa Alianza (a children's shelter) street educators. In the bus terminal in Zone 4, we found a wasted boy who was so addicted to glue and thinner that he was beginning to lose the use of his legs and extremities. He complained about not feeling well, and the other children confirmed that he had not eaten in days. We took the boy, Edvin, to the 24 hour Crisis Center. Edvin was immediately attended by a Casa Alianza doctor and kept under observation. On Thursday afternoon of last week, Edvin was transferred to the hospital as he was not responding to treatment. On this past Monday, June 2, Edvin passed away. On Tuesday he was buried in the Casa Alianza graveyard. We knew of no family. The only people who came to the burial were the other street children.

In the following account, care workers in St Petersburg report on three of many children they have rescued from the city's streets:

St Petersburg, Russia

A place in the home was … given to Denis (15), Vadim (11) and Rita (12) whose situation was extremely difficult. They came from Sverdlovsk, Siberia. Their mother sold their apartment in 1994 and the children were left homeless. At first they lived with their father. A couple of years ago, the mother moved, along with her children, into an abandoned house in the outer parts of St. Petersburg, Russia. The children had to take care of themselves and didn't go to school. They were selling bottles in the city and begging. Denis was convicted of breaking and entering, and was given a year's conditional sentence, and Rita was staying with a drug-dealing prostitute. After many arrests, the police were about to send the children to their father in Siberia. They have told us that they hate him and will run away immediately if they are sent to him.

A street child in Moscow holding a sign reading, 'help, I'm hungry'

Research

In groups These are just a few stories of the many thousands of children in the world who are, at this moment, living in destitution without care or support, facing disease and death. If you want to find out how widespread the problem is, do a search on the Internet by typing in 'street children'. You will be surprised by what you find. But be prepared also for a shock, for the plight of street children is truly horrifying and has become one of the worst social ills in the world today.

Street children campaign

As a class Dr Barnardo was a great campaigner. You could carry on his work by mounting your own campaign to raise awareness of the plight of street children around the world. Here are some ideas for campaign activities:

- Give a presentation to the school of stories, pictures and articles downloaded from the Internet. Collect statistics to show the scale of the problem. You could use the children's own words in your presentation.

- Write letters to enlist support from local people: the school governors, town councillors, your MP. You may also want to write to your local paper. You will need to put together documents laying out clearly and concisely the nature of the problem; these must be informative and accurate, and be written in a way that will hold the reader's attention.

- Raise money for charities who work with street children. Remember that all of Dr Barnardo's work depended on charitable donations.

Study the copy of the Barnardo's leaflet on page 111. How does it make its appeal? Can you use any of its techniques for your campaign?

£1 today

if you give

children like Zoe
could have
a better start
in life

Barnardos

Registered Charity No 216250

Barnardo's is a national children's charity

Barnardo's works with the most vulnerable and needy children to ensure they get what they need to develop into adults who can play a useful and valued role in society.

Currently we work with over 43,000 children, young people and their families every year providing the emotional and practical support they need. This is done via our 285 projects (mainly community based) in England, Scotland, Wales and Northern Ireland.

Over one quarter of children in the UK are brought up in poverty. Families living in unhealthy or overcrowded housing, with difficulties meeting bills and nowhere for children to play, are under continuous pressure.

Barnardo's helps disadvantaged families, providing play groups, counselling, financial advice and parenting education and support.

A family that can cope

Being a parent is one of the most important jobs there is, yet little attention is paid to preparing people for this vital role.

Barnardo's work aims to develop parents' skills and strengthen their relationships with their children.

This work includes:

- parenting groups, and one to one work through our network of family centres
- community based parenting programmes
- specialised work with parents who have particular needs

87 pence out of every £1 we spend goes directly to our vital work with children.

How your money is spent

Barnardo's needs over £1 million a week to provide support through its 285 services, for example:

- £20 pays for a child to attend a Barnardo's play group for one day
- £85 provides a day at an outdoor activity centre for a young person with disabilities
- £1000 runs a community project for a week

Every penny you give helps make the life of a child or young person in the UK a little better.

Please help us to continue our work.

4 million people have been invited to contribute...

...if you can give £1,
we could raise £4 million.
Imagine what that could do for
disadvantaged children.

Please give what you can afford.

Thank you.

Name: _____

Address: _____

_____

Postcode: _____

0644

My gift is enclosed ☐

Please tick if you do not wish to be sent more details about Barnardo's work ☐

Research resources and further reading

If you would like to do more research into the story of Dr Barnardo and the problems of child poverty, you will find the following books and Internet addresses helpful.

Barnardo's
Something Attempted Something Done by T.J.Barnardo (Shaw & Co)
Father of Nobody's Children by Norman Wymer (Hutchinson & Co)
For the Sake of the Children by June Rose (Hodder and Stoughton)

Barnardo's has a photographic and film archive containing nearly 2 million photographs from 1871 to the present day. A free brochure is available on request from: Barnardo's Head Office, Tanners Lane, Barkingside, Ilford, Essex IG6 1QG. Tel: 0181 550 8822.
Photocopies can be supplied to you if you cannot visit the archive.

Children
Mayhew's Characters edited by Peter Quennell (Spring Books)
The voices of characters in Victorian London, including the watercress girl and the pickpocket.
Children in Care by Jean S. Heywood (Routledge & Kegan Paul)
The story of the development of social services for children in need.
A Child's World by James Walvin (Penguin)
A social history of English childhood, 1800 – 1914.

Websites
Barnardo's: http://www.barnardos.org.uk
Fostering Information Line: http://www.fostering.org.uk/
Shelter: http://www.shelter.org.uk
Streetkids – Learning Resource page:
http://www.jbu.edu/business/sk.html
This page promotes awareness of the global plight of street children and those organisations and individuals that work to help them.